The Big Store

Also by Oscar Schisgall

SWASTIKA

The Big Store

by Oscar Schisgall

NEW YORK

PRENTICE-HALL INC.

To

Max Hess, Jr.

In appreciation of the many things he taught me about department stores in America

Chapter
One

As HE LISTENED to the arguments around the conference table, Conrad Selby had an impulse to call these people fools. A few, he thought, were worse than fools. They were deserters.

He could not say such things, however, while presiding over a meeting of the Board of Directors. He rapped on the long walnut table. "If you please," he said. "If you *please!*"

Looking around at the twelve directors of the Selby Department Store—nine men and three women—he tried to understand what mischief lay in their minds. It was hard. Most of them avoided his eyes.

He ran a stiff hand through thick gray hair. "Let me point out," he said, "that the proposal before the Board calls for a drastic change in our whole merchandising policy."

He paused, giving them a chance to justify what he felt was unjustifiable. But no one spoke.

Conrad Selby drew in his lips. He turned to his secretary. "Maud, let's hear the motion again."

The dark-haired woman adjusted her glasses and read, "Mr. Mark Reickert moved that the Board of Directors employ Mr. Paul Blaze of Philadelphia to become general manager of the Selby Department Store, on terms to be agreed upon between a committee of the Board and Mr. Blaze."

"Thank you." Conrad Selby sent his glance around the table. "A motion, in other words, to allow the management of Selby's to pass out of Selby hands."

His sister-in-law at the far end of the table called for the floor. Her eyes met Selby's boldly. "I second this motion. And I don't think the chair ought to make its own unfair interpretations."

It stung to hear Martha turn against him. Again he realized that the members of his own family were the real ringleaders of this insurrection. But he kept his deep voice quiet.

"Seconded by Mrs. Martha Selby," he said.

While the secretary made her notation, the conference room was silent—a big, walnut-paneled room across which the life-size portraits of the store's founders, Gordon and James Selby, faced each other from opposite walls. When the store had been remodeled a few years ago, Conrad Selby himself had supervised the decoration of this room. He was proud of it. Like his office—and his manner of living—it symbolized the dignity he liked to associate with Selby's.

From where he sat he could look at a picture of the store on the wall opposite him. It had been painted by his daughter Patrice four months ago, as a gift for his sixty-second birthday. Using the misty technique that was characteristic of all her work, Patrice had managed to create an aura of twilight beauty around the big gray building. It reminded Selby of a Childe Hassam canvas. You saw the store as through a fog—six floors high, filling a full square block in the very heart of Williston. Only Patrice, he had often thought, could have painted such a subject with affection.

Now, as he spoke, it seemed inconceivable to him that he should be fighting for his own survival in the store. He kept his eyes raised to the picture.

"As I understand it," he said, "this motion assumes I will remain president of Selby's, but in name only. The real directing head will be Paul Blaze."

Halfway down the table his brother-in-law, Mark Reickert, said, "Now hold on, Con! I never put it that way! The idea is to have Blaze work *with* you."

"I don't need anyone to work with me."

Mark Reickert started to reply but changed his mind. He was a heavy, bald man with a ponderous face. His primary interest was a chain of restaurants in Pittsburgh and Harrisburg, but he owned enough Selby stock, by inheritance from his wife, to sit on the Board. Today he had been Conrad Selby's most outspoken critic. Now, however, he seemed unable to find adequate words.

At the far end of the table Martha came to Mark's rescue. "Con," she said, "we've been doing a volume of approximately $5,000,000 a year for four years. Isn't that true?"

Selby nodded.

"I don't believe a store can forever stand still," she said. "You either go ahead or you slide back. We certainly haven't been going ahead. That's why I'm for taking this decisive step."

Conrad Selby looked at her thoughtfully. Martha was more forceful now, nearing fifty, than she had ever been. His own wife, before her death, used to say, "Sometimes I think Martha has only one god, and his name is Dividends." Maybe that was true. Yet he suspected Martha had other reasons, too, for demanding a change in Selby's management. He wished he knew what they were.

"We're simply not getting our share of local business," she said. "We're letting it slide to competition. What will Halliday's store gross this year?"

Selby had to concede, "About $15,000,000."

"There you are! A store only two blocks from our own and no bigger. Yet Halliday's grosses $15,000,000 to our $5,000,000. Why?"

Before Selby could reply Mark bent his bald head over the table and flung out, *"I'll* tell you why! Halliday's isn't afraid of promotion! Halliday's is *alive!* We're asleep!"

"Halliday's," Selby said without raising his voice, "is a bargain-basement operation."

"Call it what you like," Reickert said. "The fact is they've found the formula for doing real business: promotion! That's why I'm for Paul Blaze. A promotion man!"

Conrad Selby was relieved to see Benjamin Lork lift his hand. He knew he could count on Ben. Conservative, able, intelligent. Aside from being controller and treasurer of the store, Ben was also his son-in-law. He had married Conrad's older daughter, Grace, some nine years ago.

Ben Lork said, "I'm getting fed up with this business of comparing Halliday's with Selby's." A lean man of thirty-eight, he had reddish hair and a sharp face that bore a no-nonsense expression. "Why don't we face the fact that we're different types of stores? If we drag in Paul Blaze and his circus promotions, we're going to change the whole character of Selby's. Maybe some of you think that's good. I say it's wrong and dangerous. It means losing the kind of customers who *like* the way we do business. We'll wind up being nothing at all—except, maybe, a second-rate imitation of Halliday's."

Mark Reickert said, "Brother, if we can imitate Halliday's volume, give me imitation!"

But Ben insisted, "The kind of spectacular, bang-bang promotion we're likely to get from Blaze is not the answer to our problem. I'm against it."

"You've got a wrong impression of Paul Blaze. Ask Everett," Mark said.

Conrad Selby glanced uncertainly at his nephew. Martha's son Everett was in charge of the store's advertising and publicity—a blond, good-looking giant who retained all the physical vigor of his football days. He had ability. He worked hard and he seemed to enjoy every moment of it. But he had joined the enemy camp in this debate.

"I can tell you this about Paul," Everett said. "He does *not* go in for the circus stuff Ben's afraid of. His ideas are sound. First met him back in the Harvard School of Business Administration, and he had a lot on the ball even then. He——" Everett glanced questioningly at Conrad Selby. "Is this biographical stuff in order?"

"Go on."

"When he left Harvard he got a job at Blair's in New York. Assistant to the promotion manager. He started sparking ideas right from the start. In time he changed the whole character of their advertising. And after about six months Paul practically took over the department. Stayed with the store two years. Blair's went from nine to eleven million."

"If he was that good," Ben asked, "why did they let him go?"

"Why does anybody leave a job? He got a better offer. From Christie's in Philadelphia. And in three years Christie's went from fourteen to almost eighteen million. I say anybody who can do that for Blair's and Christie's can do a job for us!"

Conrad Selby noticed that the bronze-haired young woman at his left, Bernardine Sorel, had for some time been trying to interrupt. Twice she had raised a hand only to lower it again. Bernardine was the store's fashion co-ordinator. She had taste—you could see that in the way she dressed. And she could talk with charm and ease to any audience, serving as commentator at the store's fashion shows.

Selby asked, "Bernardine?"

The girl looked toward Everett. "I happen to know Paul Blaze," she said. "In fact, I know his former wife, too. And I have a great deal of respect for him. But it's always been my impression that Paul's the—city type, if you know what I mean."

"Williston's no village," Everett said. "He'll come if we meet his terms."

Terms. Conrad Selby's lips twisted ironically. He didn't mind the $35,000 salary Paul Blaze demanded. The store could afford that. It was the other stipulation that made him resentful: Paul's insistence on receiving a stock bonus at the end of each year, its size to depend on the increase of business he produced. This was something hard to swallow—the idea of giving Selby stock to an outsider.

But, Selby reflected, this motion need not be carried. Not if he could marshal enough resistance among these other twelve directors.

He said, "Let me point out that a man like Blaze can do a great deal of harm."

"Harm?" Mark Reickert repeated. "How?"

"He'll naturally try to surround himself with people who think the way he thinks. That could mean changes in personnel. Especially at the top level."

Selby uttered this warning with a purpose. There were nine representatives of the store's personnel on the Board—nine working directors. He saw some of them become uneasy. It was important to make them realize that the coming of Paul Blaze, of new management, might cost them their jobs. When you fought for votes you had to seize every available weapon.

Reickert said, "Nonsense! It's just as likely his coming will do the employees good. The more a store earns, the higher salaries it can pay. *Everybody* stands to profit if sales go up!"

Selby did not press the point. He had given them something to think about, he hoped.

Glancing around, he tried to appraise the strength of his support. Obviously Reickert, Martha, and her son Everett were lost to him. Just as obviously he could count on the backing of his son-in-law, Ben. But the others?

Dr. Philip Selby, playing with his pencil midway down the table, had so far said nothing. Conrad respected this cousin of his. Not only was he a successful physician; he had shown shrewdness and foresight in real estate dealings. And Selby believed Philip had enough family pride, enough faith in the store, to refuse to yield to an outsider.

Bernardine Sorel? She had a good job. What could she hope to gain from a change in the store's management? As a matter of fact, he could say the same about the other employees who sat around the table. Randolph Green, for instance, the head fashion buyer—so upset by the debate that even now he was swallowing one of his eternal white pills. And Mrs. Isabelle Rorich, Elliott Gore, Harry Manderson, Walter Bliss—all of them, in fact. Wasn't Selby himself responsible for their rise? Weren't they his protégés? Why should they vote against him?

Suddenly he felt more confident.

"Before we vote," he said, "let me assure you that nobody wants an increase in business more than I do. But I want an increase by methods that follow the spirit of Selby's. No cheap promotional stunts. I refuse to see this store turned into a spectacle. I believe that all of us working together *can* increase business. And we need no outside help."

"Con," Mark said, "you told us the same thing last year.

And the year before. Meanwhile we've stuck to our conservative policies and we haven't gone anywhere—while Halliday's keeps right on booming. . . . Let's quit talking and get action!"

And from her end of the table Martha Selby added, "I move the question. A closed ballot, please."

Selby sent her a sidelong glance. A closed ballot meant nobody need worry about offending the president by openly voting against him; nobody need worry about jeopardizing his job.

Whatever Martha's purpose might be, he couldn't refuse the request. He said, "Very well. You have paper before you. Write 'yes' if you approve of the motion to hire Paul Blaze. Write 'no' if you disapprove."

As the directors picked up pencils he glanced at the portraits of the founders. The management of the Selby store had descended from them to his own hands some twenty years ago. He had always felt it was a trust to be kept within the family. After him? Perhaps his son-in-law, Ben Lork. Or his nephew, Everett Selby. That could be determined in time. To turn management over to an outsider, however, would mark the beginning of disintegration. His whole being rebelled against the idea. It was monstrous to believe the Selbys were no longer able to look after their own affairs.

He wrote *No*.

The folded ballots were passed along the table. He asked Bernardine Sorel and Ben, who sat closest to him, to serve as tellers. While they unfolded the papers, Selby lit a cigarette.

Maybe, in the past five years, he had not given the store the most vigorous leadership possible—if, by vigor, you meant the kind of leadership Halliday's had. And maybe, since the death of his wife, he had sought a more quiet, contemplative life in the store as well as in his home. But one thing he knew he *had* done: he had retained the essential character of Selby's. The store had dignity. People trusted it as they trusted the First National Bank. They had faith in its integrity, in the quality of everything it offered. Could you call that failure?

Ben announced in a tight voice, "We're ready with the result."

"Yes?" Selby said.

"The motion to hire Paul Blaze as general manager has been carried by a vote of 9 to 4."

Generally, when Conrad Selby left the store at 5:45, his chauffeur waited at the side-street exit to drive him to his home on Warwick Hill. Today, however, he found his daughter Patrice at the door. She sat in her own red car, her short-clipped blond hair hatless, the collar of a plaid sports coat turned up in a casual way.

To see her here did not surprise Selby. Rallying to a lost cause, he thought as he got into the car. He could tell she knew what had happened from the way she kissed him. At a moment like this he could be grateful for the fact that Patrice was still with him, still unmarried, still part of his own life.

"Dad, I'm sorry," she said.

He did not answer.

"How can they be such fools?" She sounded bitter. "Don't they realize what you've done for them? For the store? For——"

He patted her hand. "Let's not hold a wake."

She studied his lined face, and her eyes flashed in anger.

She started the car with a jerk. "You're not going to sit back and *let* this Paul Blaze take over, are you?"

"No, I don't intend to—abdicate." Selby leaned back. He was tired of thinking, of arguing. The overhead traffic light changed, and he took off his hat as Patrice turned into Main Street.

At this hour, with the dusk deepening, Main Street was crowded with home-going traffic. Its neon signs were ablaze. In the block ahead the two-story-high letters that flashed "Halliday's" filled the street with alternate flares of red and yellow. There was a lurid, explosive quality in each change of color. He thought of the steady-glowing sign outside his own store, and even in this comparison, it seemed to him, there was symbolism.

"Patsy," he said, "what's got into people?"

"Ingratitude!"

"No, it's not that. It's—it's a change in the way they think about business. . . . Doing well isn't good enough any more. What you've got to do now is beat the next fellow. . . . What's a $5,000,000 business when somebody else is doing $15,000,000? Unless you're on top, you're a flop. Directors won't tolerate second place. . . ."

He spoke slowly, and Patrice knew he was talking to himself rather than to her. Maybe it would do him good to get these things said. She crossed the bridge at the end of Main Street, over the railroad tracks, and turned left into Warwick Road. From here a long, uphill drive wound to their white hilltop home two miles away. It was dark now. She kept her eyes on the path of the headlights.

"Even the language of stores has changed," Selby said. "Who speaks about dignity any more? Or integrity? Or respectability? Words like that are out of date. The only word that counts today is—promotion. *Sell!* Faster and faster. More and more. Build up that volume or step aside for somebody who can." Selby's face hardened. "Well, I won't step aside. It's still the Selby store. It'll still be run by Selby standards."

"As long as you don't let them push you around!"

He looked at the firm, straight lines of his daughter's face. Her aggressiveness often surprised him. He used to amuse himself by thinking that Patrice lived in a remote world of her own. He had given her a year of study in Rome, a year in Paris, two years in New York. Now magazines were using her paintings on their covers; at twenty-five she was an established artist. Yet there was nothing detached or unworldly in Patrice, nothing of the impractical dreamer. She was blunt and decisive; as deeply steeped in the traditions of the store, he suspected, as he was himself.

"I don't know why Paul Blaze should even want to come to Williston," she said. "If he's so good, why doesn't a big city store grab him? What makes a man leave the big leagues to play in the minors?"

"The big leagues," Selby said, "don't always pay $35,000 plus a stock bonus."

"The Board was crazy to vote him stock!"

"Those were the only terms on which he'd come."

"What was this meeting—a Munich? I'm going to dislike this man. I dislike him already—sight unseen!"

"That's silly, Pat. The situation isn't his fault. It's the Board that did it. If it weren't Blaze, they'd bring in another promotion man."

She swung the car into their driveway. The white house was wide and sprawling, its lower windows lit behind their curtains.

"We'll have to accept him," Selby said. "The problem is to—*control* him. . . ."

Chapter
Two

IN THE DINING ROOM of Philadelphia's Hotel Clayton, Paul Blaze ate the first calm meal he had known in weeks. The roast beef was tender; the sauce on the broccoli had exactly the right tang of lemon; the baked potato was hot enough to melt its butter. Paul enjoyed the dinner—which was hardly true of his companion. Edmond C. Christie, one of the three brothers who owned the Christie Department Store, looked irritated. An enormous, freckled man with bristling red hair, he peered at Paul through thick-lensed glasses.

"I don't get it," he said. "I thought you were happy with us."

"Sure," Paul said. "Had three good years in your store."

"So?"

"The point is—where am I getting?"

"A man can't go higher than the top," Christie argued. "You're practically *at* the top. What else do you want?"

"I've told you, Ed. A share in ownership."

"That's impossible."

"Exactly. Which is why I'm going to Selby's. In a year I'll own a block of Selby stock."

Edmond Christie watched Paul Blaze cut his meat. His

eyes were fixed on the thin quick hands, their long fingers as positive as a pianist's. His gaze rose to Paul's face—lean, dark-complexioned, taut in a way that betrayed tension. Yet there had been no tension in his voice.

Christie said, "I suppose it's none of my business, but are they paying you as much salary as we are?"

"More."

"In a town like Williston?"

"Maybe that's why. To make it attractive."

"They certainly must want you." The red-haired man hesitated, then bent forward. "Paul, if it's a matter of pay, you know damn well we'd meet their price."

"Ed, any deal that doesn't include a chance of ownership doesn't interest me. I'm sick of working for some other guy's future. I've got to think of myself."

"That sounds——"

"Mercenary? Okay, so I'm mercenary. When you get into your thirties, and you've worked your head off, with not much to show for it except in other people's bank accounts, you get to be mercenary in a big way."

Christie pushed his plate aside. "Seems to me you're building up a gripe which isn't justified," he said. "Apart from the fact that you've been earning $25,000 a year with us, you've got plenty to show for your work. I mean in satisfaction, in accomplishment, in reputation. As to the money itself——"

"Money isn't everything, huh?" A trace of sarcasm came into Paul's tones. "Drop it, Ed. Only two types give you this money-isn't-everything routine. The kind that's got so much it can *afford* contempt for money; I can't. And there's the other kind—the failures. They go noble, try to make you overlook their failure by saying they're shooting for something bigger than money. . . . Well, I'm not. I *want* money. I want the kind you've got—invested, paying dividends, representing something I *own*."

Christie's laugh was faintly sardonic. "What makes you think you'll get it at Selby's?"

"My contract."

"It's a family-owned store. They may give you a small stock bonus, but if it's a real slice of the business you want, you'll never get it." He leaned back, and again his laugh was cynical. "Only way to get into a family business is to marry into it."

Paul grinned. "It's an idea. What better reason could a man have for marrying?"

Though the words came lightly, Christie caught the sting in them. It occurred to him that even after an association of three years he knew little about Paul Blaze's unfortunate marriage and divorce; these were things Paul never discussed. All Christie knew was that it had been a wartime marriage which had collapsed shortly after Paul had got out of uniform.

A waiter removed the dishes. While they ordered coffee and dessert, Christie lit a cigar.

"This contract with Selby's," he said. "I suppose the stock bonus is adjusted to a sliding scale? The higher you push Selby's volume, the more stock you get?"

"That's right."

"In that case, Paul, take my advice and watch yourself." Christie seemed to find satisfaction in uttering the warning. "Once you start rolling too fast, they'll get scared. Slap you down. I know Conrad Selby. He doesn't give his store away."

Paul Blaze lit a cigarette. "Nobody's going to slap me down, Ed."

"Okay, boy. Dream on." Edmond Christie contemplated

the ashes of his cigar. "Just remember Conrad Selby is as smart an operator as you are. *I* think you're in for one hell of a jolt."

Later, alone in his small suite, Paul tried to concentrate on a report drawn up for the Controllers' Congress of the National Retail Dry Goods Association. He sat in a deep chair, slippered feet propped up on a coffee table. The booklet in his lap lay open to statistical pages marked:

Merchandising and Operating Results
Department Stores—Annual Sales $10,000,000 to
$20,000,000—Typical Performance

Usually he had no difficulty in analyzing such statistics. Mark-ons, mark-downs, number of transactions, number of stock turns, newspaper costs, salespeoples' salaries, delivery expense—these and others like them were problems with which he lived twenty-four hours a day. He found them exciting, absorbing, a constant challenge to ingenuity. To cope with them gave him a sense of fulfillment, and when people said he worked too hard, he could only smile. Where was the self-punishment in doing something you enjoyed?

Tonight, however, he found it impossible to absorb the figures.

He felt uneasy, and he couldn't understand why. Surely it wasn't because he had decided to leave Christie's. There was no reason to be nervous about that. A good business opportunity. A step upward. The only emotion it warranted was satisfaction.

With his hand lying on the page of figures, Paul gazed unseeingly at the picture of a windmill on the hotel wall. He had lived with that print for almost three years; and like most of the hotel art he had known, it had registered on his mind no more sharply than the wallpaper. Had he shut his eyes, he could have described it only in the vaguest terms.

Presently he realized that the thing which was making him nervous had, like the picture, been with him for years, unnoticed, unobtrusive, yet ever a part of him. He was nervous because he was at last taking a giant step toward something he had promised himself since boyhood.

"Paul," his father had told him in a moment of bitterness, "don't make the mistake of spending all your life working for somebody else. If you want to amount to something, the trick is to get other people to work for *you!*"

Normally Paul Blaze avoided thinking about such incidents in his childhood. Too many of those memories were dispiriting. Not that there weren't also pleasant moments to recall; no boyhood could fail to leave its wistful souvenirs, and his own, he supposed, were as good as most. It was easy to exaggerate difficulties. Yet there must have been many families in Malden, Massachusetts, worse off than the Blazes.

As a matter of fact, the Blaze family had been respectably middle-class. During the eighteen years they lived in the rented apartment on the upper floor of the Lock Street house, Elmer Blaze probably earned as much as most of his neighbors. The family had never known poverty—only an endless striving for something that had never materialized: a mysterious state known as "financial security" which, like Nirvana, Paul had long ago learned, few families ever achieved.

It wasn't his father's fault. It wasn't anybody's fault. He remembered his father as a quiet, friendly man—lanky, sandy-haired, almost shy. He should have been a pastor or a worker for some welfare organization, for he had a deep and instinctive sympathy for the underdog. Instead, he traveled for a firm of Boston shoe manufacturers, selling through a territory that covered half a dozen states from New Jersey down through the Carolinas.

Toward the end, Paul remembered, his father wore a silver watch-charm, in the shape of a shoe, given to commemorate twenty-five years of service with the company. But one evening, after looking at it a long time, Elmer Blaze had suddenly detached the thing from his chain. White of face, he had gone to the open window and flung the charm into the darkness.

"No, I haven't gone crazy!" he'd said. "Why should any man want to wear a symbol of failure?"

If he considered himself a failure, it was because he had all his life talked about going into business for himself. And he had never been able to do it. With three children to rear and with his wife hospitalized for years before her death, he had never managed to accumulate enough capital for the venture. As a result, the Blaze home was filled with an atmosphere of frustration—and it was this Paul so clearly recalled. The awful sense of being thwarted by life, of resentment against fate.

Of course, like his brother and sister, Paul had run out that night to search for the charm. It seemed a sinful waste to throw such a thing away. He had found it, all right, in the light of a street lamp near the next house.

"Very well, keep it, then," his father had said. "Maybe it will remind you of what to avoid."

Somewhere among his belongings Paul still had the tiny silver shoe. Now and then, turning up in some odd place, it gave him a twinge.

Yet, considered in proper perspective, his father could

scarcely be called a failure; certainly not in the kind of family he had raised. Paul's younger brother, Greg, was practicing medicine in Poughkeepsie. His sister Anne, now the wife of a prosperous sawmill operator, had a lovely old house near Bangor, Maine, and two lively, healthy boys. So, by and large, you might say the children of Elmer Blaze were doing well. Had he lived, Elmer Blaze would have been pleased.

But *Paul* wasn't pleased. Not, any rate, with himself.

From the beginning he had been frightened by his father's frustration. He certainly didn't want it repeated in his own life. And the only way he knew of avoiding it was to have money. Plenty of money.

He started his campaign for it early by seeking after-school jobs—the kind of jobs many of his friends also sought: delivering orders for grocers, butchers; selling ice cream at a baseball park; washing cars. He never stopped working in odd hours. Years later, when he won a Harvard scholarship, he devoted his vacations to selling in Filene's department store.

But he remembered his father's warning that you couldn't win security by working for others. The trick was to make others work for *you*. . . .

Moreover, the whole wretched affair with Janet Carver served to emphasize the point. If he'd had some sort of income at the time—even enough to carry him comfortably through a year or two—he might still have been married.

He'd met Janet while he was in the army, at the Massachusetts camp. She'd been a slim, red-haired WAC whose uniform could not hide a single curve of her beauty. At the beginning he'd had to take his turn with a dozen other young officers in getting dates, but gradually he'd won more and more of her time for himself. And when he'd got orders to go overseas there had seemed but one thing to do. He'd put the question to Janet bluntly. She hesitated only a moment, then came into his arms. Within four days they were married.

In England, and later in France, Paul kept telling himself you couldn't expect a girl as spirited as Janet to spend every evening and every week end reading magazines in WAC barracks. Besides, she wrote him honestly about everything she did, everybody she met. It was all above-board.

That Brooklyn fellow who was making a fortune out of his nickel-plating plant, for instance. Bruce Gilette. She met him at a party while she had a week-end pass. He'd come with a girl named Bernardine Sorel, but within two days he sent Janet a telegram. Could he take her to dinner next time she was off duty?

After that she mentioned Gilette in one or two letters, then stopped writing about him. In fact, Paul heard no more about the man till after the war, when he came home with nothing worse than the mark of a shrapnel slash in his thigh.

That was when he told Janet he planned to use his GI rights to take a course at the Harvard School of Business Administration.

She stared. "But Paul, it takes *a year!*"

"Worth it."

"What about *me?* What am I supposed to do for a whole year? Get a job? Support myself?"

"Well——"

"I thought when you came back I'd finally be able to live like a married woman. Have a home. Get away from a desk and a boss——"

She would have said none of this, he knew, if there had been any kind of income. . . .

Paul did his best to ease Janet's dismay. He thought he succeeded; and for a while, after he went back to Harvard, they lived in a couple of rented rooms on the edge of Cambridge, and he imagined there would be no trouble. Janet actually started looking for a job.

And then she stunned him with the announcement that she was going to Las Vegas for a divorce; that their hurried marriage had been a mistake; that she intended to marry Bruce Gilette. . . .

Paul wrenched the memory out of his mind. He got up, tossed aside the booklet of statistics. He lit a cigarette and walked restlessly about the room.

Janet, like his father, had taught him an irrefutable lesson: in this hard, practical world only one kind of man could really seize happiness—the man with an income that *insured* happiness. People like Edmond Christie had it. People like Conrad Selby had it. People smart enough to get their hands on property that paid dividends. Damn it, Paul thought, he'd have it, too!

Chapter
Three

PAUL BLAZE signed his contract with the Selby Department Store in March. A week later, on Sunday, April 1st, he drove his black convertible into Williston and checked into the Williston Hotel. Another home, another hotel, he reflected wryly as bellhops carried his seven grips into the elevator. He had been living in hotels for years, ever since his divorce from Janet.

While the elevator rose, he realized that this was an unsatisfactory way to live—a thought which had troubled him hundreds of times. He ought to have firmer roots, a home, a more substantial, more gracious existence. There was no reason to continue this unanchored hotel life. Sooner or later, here in Williston, he ought to have an apartment of his own.

He knew, however, that such a change would have to wait. To find and furnish an apartment, to convert it to a home with the help of an able housekeeper—all this must take time which he would not be able to afford immediately.

"The whole store's on edge," Everett Selby had warned him. "They visualize you as a sort of human dynamo, and they expect plenty of quick action."

Paul smiled over this as he followed a bellhop into the

two-room suite. If the personnel of Selby's was anticipating an explosion, he would disappoint them. In fact, his very personality might disappoint them, for he knew he violated many popular concepts associated with high-pressure sales promotion. For one thing, he had no nervous stomach ailment, no wild-eyed zeal. He generally managed to look calm. A week ago, when he had come to Williston to sign the contract and meet the Board of Directors, he had told them, "Don't expect me to be one of those ulcerated monkeys you see in TV dramas. My job here is to produce business, not convulsions."

The fact that he was outwardly calm, however, could not deny inner tension. One of Paul's principal commodities was energy, and this he burned up at a prodigious rate. Its constant expenditure kept his body lean—too lean. He was just under six-feet tall, yet he weighed less than one hundred sixty. This often worried him, so that in spurts of concern he forced himself to eat more than he would normally consume. It did no good. Paul Blaze, tall, brown-haired, intense, would always be too thin.

When he had unpacked, he went to the corner window to stare down at Main Street. On Sunday nights its neon lights were dimmed; it had an empty, abandoned look. Two blocks away he could see the great gray mass of the Selby store. He surveyed it now with the dubious appraisal a man might give to a mountain he planned to climb.

He had no illusions about this job. It would not be easy. After signing his contract he had spent a week end with Everett Selby; and he had gathered, from both Everett and his mother, Martha, that the president and the controller of the store resented his coming. His presence would be a perpetual reminder of their own ineffectuality.

"But you needn't worry," Martha Selby had said. "The majority of the Board stands ready to back you."

Paul was uneasy about the situation. He'd have problems enough in sales promotion without having to overcome resistance from top executives.

But now, as he looked at the huge building two blocks away, he remembered that he was principally concerned with his own future. *If I've got to fight them, I'll fight them,* he thought. And he turned away, feeling ready for whatever might happen. . . .

At nine the next morning he stood before the bedroom mirror, knotting a maroon tie, when the telephone rang. He picked it up to hear Everett Selby's voice.

"Morning!" Everett was always cheerful. As far back as Harvard, Paul recalled, nothing had ever been able to quell his good humor. He said, "I'm down in the lobby, Paul. Committee of one to show you your new office."

"Be right with you."

Paul stepped around the remnants of breakfast on a table, put on the jacket of a blue, pin-stripe suit. This was his one fetish—clothes. There were eighteen custom-tailored suits in his closet, and he had two more on order. The handkerchief that went into the breast pocket received a final pat. He drew the last stroke of a comb through his brown hair, knowing it would be rumpled again within half an hour. Then he got his hat and coat and went down.

Everett greeted him with a grin and a hearty handclasp. "Well, boy, this is it. *Der Tag!*"

Outside they had to bend against a blustery wind as they walked the two blocks to the store. The gusts were bringing the first spatterings of April rain, and Everett glanced unhappily at the sky.

"Couldn't have picked a lousier day to start," he said. "A wet Monday. The store'll be a graveyard." Then he asked, "Did my uncle call you last night?"

"No."

"Chances are you're in for a clear-the-decks conference this morning."

"Good. I'd like a few things cleared."

"You'll find he's a great guy, my uncle. Quiet, dignified, restrained. But when he's quietest—look out. That's when he's apt to cut loose with a haymaker."

Paul tried to appear casual. "I'll keep my guard up."

They were outside the Selby store now, passing the show windows. He sent a glance at each one, most of them featuring women's spring apparel. They left him unimpressed. Display without inspiration, he thought. He rounded the corner, and here, on Fourth Street, the windows exhibited lamps, shoes, housewares, haberdashery. He still thought them dull. And a dull window was as futile as a sleeping salesperson.

Beyond the last window they entered the store by way of the employees' entrance. Though Selby's would not open for business until 9:30, salespeople were already removing the long coverings of cheesecloth that protected counters overnight. During this process the main floor had a ghostly look, but it was a familiar sight to Paul. It made him feel at home. As they walked past the cosmetic counters, with their profusion of scents, he couldn't help noting that employees—called "co-workers" at Selby's—all paused for a curious look at him.

Everett whispered with a chuckle, "Every single one of them is wondering what the hell happens from here on in."

Paul thought, *So am I.*

He wished others would be as easy to get along with as this amiable young Viking with the blond crew-cut. He liked Everett. He liked Everett's wife, Betty, and their two children, whom he had met on his week-end visit. But he knew he'd be confronted with difficulties in the case of Conrad Selby and Ben Lork, and he could hardly anticipate this kind of easy friendship from them.

Though the escalators were already in operation, they took an elevator to the sixth floor. Everett said, "Later I'll show you some newspaper clips. We sent out releases about your coming. Locally you got quite a press."

Apparently they were the first to reach the sixth-floor executive offices. Going along a gray-walled corridor, they passed one empty room after another. When they came to the last two doors Everett said, "The one on the right is my uncle's. The one on the left is yours."

Paul stood on the threshold, his hands in his coat pockets. His was not a big office, but it was attractively appointed: a bleached-wood desk, drapery-framed windows, a dictating machine, a brown-leather couch and three deep brown-leather chairs.

Everett clapped him on the shoulders. "Luck, boy!"

Paul asked, "Whose office *was* this?"

"Nobody's. Used to be an alcove off the big conference room. We had it partitioned."

Paul was grateful for that. Little things—like moving a man to make room for another—could cause personal friction and resentment, and he was glad to learn he'd be spared this concern. He hung his hat and coat in a closet.

"Anything I can do before I leave you to the wolves?" Everett asked.

"Not a thing, thanks."

"See you later, then."

When Everett was gone, and he sat down for the first time

. . . First, the cafeteria management asks that you remember, please, to return empty trays to the racks. A number of co-workers have been forgetting that lately, and it has given the cafeteria a lot of unnecessary work. It has also delayed those co-workers who have had to wait for clean trays and clean places at the tables. Remember, please! Return your trays to the racks!"

"Fascinating, isn't it?" Bernardine murmured.

Paul smiled. Some annoyances were the same in all stores—the human element.

"And the second announcement," the voice went on, "is one of the most important it has ever been my privilege to make. This is the day Mr. Paul Blaze becomes general manager of Selby's. I have been told he is already in his office. I hope he is listening, because now, on behalf of all seven hundred Selby co-workers, I want to wish Mr. Blaze the best of luck and success, and I want to promise him our full co-operation. Welcome, Mr. Blaze! We hope you'll like it here. We all look forward to working with you. . . . It is now 9:30. The gong will sound in ten seconds."

A routine announcement of welcome. It could have happened in any store. Yet, staring at the ash tray on the desk, Paul was strangely moved. . . .

As a bell signaled the formal opening of the store, Bernardine said, "Well, there's a job or two I've got to do. Yell any time you need my help."

A few minutes after she left, Conrad Selby came into the office. Selby lowered his long body into one of the brown leather chairs. He inspected the room with quick, comprehensive eyes, like a stage manager checking props. "Hope you'll find everything you want here," he said. "If we've overlooked anything, just talk to Maud Heller."

"Thank you."

"When Ben comes, we'll lay out a few plans of procedure. I'd like him to be in on that. I suppose you've decided how you want to start?"

"First I'd like to familiarize myself with the store. Also, dig into sales records."

"Ben will give you those." Selby took a cigar from his vest pocket, held it unlit between his fingers. "Meanwhile, suppose I give you a fill-in on a few things. Especially our physical plant."

"I'd appreciate that."

"It's a completely modern store, of course. Improvements like the air-conditioning, the fluorescent lighting, the escalators, the public address system—all are the latest kind, installed within the past few years. So is the general layout of sales space. By the way, up to the time we remodeled, our warehouse—which is to say about 60 per cent of our stock—used to be in a building over on Hillside Avenue. We had stock boys running back and forth all day long. You've noticed our present system?"

"Yes, indeed." On his previous visit Paul had observed that the store had adopted some of the best layout features of modern merchandising. Selling space did not occupy the full area of every floor. Partitions walled off a twenty-foot-wide perimeter around the sides. Beyond the partitions were work rooms, fitting rooms, stock rooms. Thus no salesperson had to go more than a few steps to bring an article out of stock.

"Four years ago," Selby went on, "we modernized our charge, billing and accounting systems, too. We now use the Charge-o-phone. And cycle billing. You're starting with *every* modern tool we could install."

Across his desk Paul studied the tall, gray-haired presi-

dent with puzzled eyes. Was Selby supplying this information
in order to be helpful? Or was he, in effect, saying, *I built all
this. I installed it all. Everything you will use is my doing. Remember that.*

"There are other general facts you should know," Selby
continued—impassive. "We now have 28,000 charge customers.
Ben will tell you that approximately 50 per cent of our business
is done with them. . . . Also, I suppose you should know about
the store's outside real estate holdings. We own the parking lot on
Euclid Avenue. And we own the brick building next to the
lot, which we maintain for workshops and the co-workers' convenience. Its basement is occupied by our carpentry shop, our
glass shop, and our printing plant. We build our own displays
and we print all our own signs and placards. The main floor
has the co-workers' cafeteria, and the floor above has their rest
and recreation rooms. Also, we run our own garage on Fifth
Street. It services a fleet of seventeen delivery trucks which——"

He must have noticed that Paul's attention had shifted
to the door. Glancing over his shoulder, Selby saw Patrice,
blond and slim and straight in her blue belted raincoat. She
had driven him down this morning.

He rose. "My daughter Patrice," he said. "Pat, Mr. Blaze."

Rising, Paul was somewhat disconcerted. He had heard
about Patrice during his week end with Everett, as he had
learned much of the family's background. But he wasn't prepared for anyone so striking, so compactly and nicely put together.

"How do you do, Mr. Blaze?" Her eyes went over him
quickly.

"Good to meet you," he said. He motioned to the couch.
"Join us?"

Patrice not only sat down; she threw off her coat, crossed

her legs, lit a cigarette. While her father resumed discussing the physical attributes of Selby's, she appraised Paul Blaze with eyes so frank and direct and curious that he found himself repeatedly glancing at her, becoming self-conscious. A damned good-looking girl, he thought, but he wished she wouldn't dissect him like a specimen on a slide.

Finally Selby looked at his watch. He got up and said, "Let me see if Ben's in." He left, and Paul found himself alone with the girl. She still seemed to be assessing him.

"Miss Selby," he said, "suppose I save you a lot of wondering."

"How?"

"Age thirty-four. Height 5 feet 11½. Weight, not enough. Eyes gray. I was born in Malden, just outside Boston. Politically I'm an independent."

A flush came into her face. She looked at the cigarette. "Sorry. Didn't realize I was being so obvious."

"Quite all right. Have I skipped anything you'd like to know?"

"I was simply trying to decide how you and Dad are going to get along."

"No reason we shouldn't, is there?"

"Depends. On how much you try to disrupt the—old order."

"As I understand it," he said, "I wasn't hired to let things stand as they are."

"That's why I'm worried."

Paul shrugged. "Your father looks like a reasonable man. So, I hope, am I. We'll click." And he added with greater assurance, "After all, we're both interested in the same thing—boosting business."

"But there's a difference," Patrice reminded him. "A difference of attitude, of approach."

"A difference big enough to cause friction?"

"Well—disagreement. . . . But there's no point in discussing that. I'm sure you're as well aware of the situation as anyone."

"I'm not certain I follow you. What do you mean by a difference of attitude?"

"Well, this whole thing has no—*emotional* meaning for you."

"Hasn't it?"

"Another store, another job—how much *can* it mean? Your whole life isn't bound up in Selby's, like his."

Paul leaned toward her. His voice tightened. "You're wrong. I've got a lot at stake in Selby's."

"I know. A block of stock. . . . Well, if you want advice from somebody who knows, go easy, Mr. Blaze."

"Afraid I wouldn't get very far by holding back."

"On the contrary. You might get much further."

Selby came back then, his reddish-haired son-in-law behind him, and the puzzling discussion had to be dropped.

Ben's handshake was firm. Paul felt about him as he had at the Board meeting; Ben Lork might turn out to be an antagonist, but he would always be outspoken.

Now Patrice rose, throwing her coat over her arm. She said to her father, "See you later. I'll be down in art-goods for a while."

She nodded to her brother-in-law and to Paul; and he had a vague feeling of irritation as she left. Would he have to cope with Selby's articulate daughter, too? How much, he wondered, would *she* be interfering here? And why should she imagine this job had no emotional significance for him?

He pushed the annoyance aside. Patrice Selby was not an integral part of the store. It was ridiculous to waste time on futile resentments. Too much waited to be done. . . .

Chapter

Four

IT WAS Paul's purpose, when he sat down in Selby's office with the president and the controller, to do more listening than talking. He glanced around. The room was very much like his own, except for a couple of paintings. He looked at them closely. Pennsylvania landscapes with a curiously mystical quality, as though seen through a haze. "My daughter Patrice's work," Selby said, not without pride. Paul liked them. The girl had more than talent. She had a distinctive quality he could not help admiring.

When he turned back to Selby and Lork, the gray-haired man was lighting a cigar. His son-in-law sat tapping the end of a pencil on the arm of his chair.

"Suppose we first consider our general objectives," Selby said, tossing his match into a tray. For some ten minutes he kept the talk focused on the store's potentialities. Then he said, "Your primary job, Blaze, is of course to increase our volume. I'm sure you've studied our figures. What approximate goal have you set?"

"For the first year? Six to seven million."

"And ultimately?"

"Twenty to twenty-five million."

It was as if Paul had uttered something absurd. It caused a visible start. Ben Lork said, "You're not serious. We're in no position to shoot that high."

Selby, for whose poise Paul was developing respect, seemed more amused than surprised. "Even Halliday's, with all its reckless promotion schemes, can't reach twenty million," he pointed out.

"I'm not basing my estimate on Halliday's," Paul said. "I'm basing it on Williston's real buying power."

Because they were skeptical, he felt compelled to defend his judgment. He bent forward, tapping his right index finger into his left palm. Whenever he talked like this, justifying a point, Paul became intense. Every bone under his skin made its own sharp line.

"Williston's population is over 160,000," he said. "A few hours from here—in Allentown, with a population of only 100,000—a store no bigger than Selby's is hitting around $20,-000,000 every year. Certainly the per capita buying power here is no less than Allentown's. You have more industries in Williston and 18,000 more people employed. I got that from your mayor's report. If *Allentown* can support a $20,000,000 store, why can't Williston? What's impractical in shooting at that figure?"

"It would mean a wholly different kind of operation," Selby said.

"Principally, it would mean stepped-up promotion," Paul replied. "Increased advertising. Publicity—the kind that'll make people think about Selby's, talk about Selby's, turn to Selby's. It *can* be done. Selby's already has the advantage of being the oldest department store in Williston. It's an institution."

"Which brings up a serious point," Ben Lork said.

"There's many a promotion scheme we've turned down because it didn't fit Selby's *character*. Remember we've got fifty-five years of conservative tradition behind us. I believe tradition has a definite dollar-and-cents value."

"I'd be the last to sell tradition short."

"I realize the Board expects you to look forward, not backward," Ben conceded. "And I'll go along with that—up to a point. But not, Blaze, if we go in for—for circus ballyhoo to stimulate business. Williston isn't Philadelphia or New York. More conservative. If we ever did anything undignified, we'd be condemned by every church and civic organization in town."

Paul took a cigarette from his pocket. "Why don't we hold off speculating on the kind of ideas I'll get till I actually get a few? That'll be after I know the store. . . . Meanwhile, I'd like a run-down on some of the departments."

Selby said, "Quite naturally most departments are in a state of suspense these days, waiting to see what's going to happen. Ben can give you the figures."

And the controller began to talk. . . .

This morning, down on the second floor, in an office behind a side-wall partition, Selby's head fashion buyer, Randolph Green, sat in conference with Bernardine Sorel. They were planning spring fashion shows and going over invoices of goods still to be delivered, when the telephone rang.

"New York, Mr. Green," the store's switchboard operator said. "Mr. Morris Hein of Cluss & Hein."

Randolph Green sent a quick glance at Bernardine. He

wished he could be alone for this conversation. But there was nothing to be done about it. "All right," he said. "Put Mr. Hein on."

A moment later he heard a man's cautious voice: "Ranny?"

"Yes, Morris?"

"I just got the news. What's *happening* down there?"

"Too early to tell."

"I don't like it, Ranny."

"Nothing to worry about."

"You know what happened to us in Philadelphia, don't you?"

Green sent an uneasy look at Bernardine's bent head. He said, "No, Morris. How d'you mean?"

"We used to sell Christie's. A fair account. Then this guy Blaze comes in. All of a sudden we don't get a nickel's worth of Christie business."

Green said, "Morris, this isn't Christie's. And *I'm* still here."

"That's why I'm calling. We're counting on you, Ranny."

Green forced confidence into his voice. "Believe me, Morris, everything'll be okay. I'll be in New York next week as usual. See you then."

"I wouldn't like to feel like a sucker, Ranny. Thrown out. Holding the bag."

"You won't. Everything'll work out. Take my word for it, Morris. . . . 'By, now. Next week."

He put down the telephone. When he turned back to Bernardine the buyer took a handkerchief from his breast pocket, dried his forehead. The girl eyed him curiously.

"Cluss & Hein," he said with impatience. "Scared about new management. Afraid Blaze may cross them off our list."

Bernardine noted his damp forehead, but she said nothing.

Green was a good-looking man, well proportioned, well dressed, with thick dark hair parted in the middle and flowing back smoothly around his temples. At the age of thirty-six he could point to an eleven-year association with the Selby store. In fact, at the last Anniversary Banquet—an event which occurred annually on the eve of the store's Anniversary Sale—he had made an amiable speech in which he'd acknowledged his deep personal indebtedness to Selby's. The store had enabled him to bring comfort and well-being to his wife and two children, and, he had added, he looked forward to long years of continued satisfaction in his work. "And now that I'm on the Board of Directors," he had said, concluding the speech with laughter, "I can practically *vote* myself satisfaction!"

He began again to discuss the pending fashion shows, but within five minutes the telephone rang a second time.

"New York again, Mr. Green," the operator said. "Mr. Herbert Shantz of Shantz Coats."

Green said testily, "Okay, okay."

A moment later Herb Shantz was telling him, "Ranny, I'm looking at page 11 in *Women's Wear*. About this new management. What the hell gives?"

Green said, "A new general manager, that's all."

"It could be bad, Ranny."

"Nonsense."

"This guy Blaze don't know us from a hole in the wall."

"*I* know you, Herb. I'm still buying." His tone changed. "Look, I'm in conference. Expect to be in New York next week. I'll talk to you then."

"We could use some quick business, Ranny."

"I understand. See you next week. And quit worrying."

When he put the telephone down, Bernardine glanced

again at his damp forehead. She said dryly, "Take it easy, Ran."

"Damn fools!" Green snapped out his handkerchief. "Do they think we're going to turn our backs on every source that ever sold us? Just because Paul Blaze is in?"

She watched him mop his forehead. She watched him take a white pill from a bottle in his drawer, swallow it. A wry quirk came to her lips. "Let's get on with this," she said. . . .

Before the morning was over Green had several other calls, all of a similar kind. Finally, alone at his desk, he stared at the picture of his wife and sons. He didn't actually see the silver-framed photograph. He was thinking of Morris Hein and Herb Shantz and the others like them.

What worried him was not the practice he had so long followed with these firms. After all, every man was entitled to look out for himself. His anxiety rose from something else:

Suppose Paul Blaze did decide to change the basic Selby lines, to deal with other firms?

Randolph Green rose. He began to pace his small office, pushing a nervous hand through thick hair. He had a deep and mordant fear that became steadily worse. . . .

Everett Selby was by all odds the busiest desk-man in the store. From 9:30 to 5:30 he saw buyer after buyer, merchandise manager after merchandise manager. They crowded his office, clamoring for newspaper space to advertise their departments. They brought along samples and layouts and mats. They wanted to co-ordinate their advertising allotments with window displays, with special buys, with the weather, with the day of the week. And Everett, as the final court of appeals, settled their claims and demands while answering calls on three telephones.

He loved the confusion. He thrived on it. The greater the excitement, the happier he felt, and so he had the reputation of being good-humored under pressure. There was a sense of power in deciding the advertising destinies of Selby's various departments.

This morning he found additional zest in his job. The releases he had sent to the press concerning Selby's new general manager were bringing results. In Williston the *Reporter* and the *News* had each run Paul Blaze's picture and a sizable story. New York and Philadelphia papers had, of course, been less responsive, though there were short items in most business pages under *New Appointments*. The best New York story had run in the department store section of *Women's Wear*—three full paragraphs.

As a result, telegrams of good wishes to the new general manager were coming from manufacturers everywhere. Everett experienced elation in seeing the pile grow on his desk, as if he were personally responsible for this. By noon he had more than forty telegrams, and he took them in to Paul's office.

"Have a look," he said.

With his initial conference behind him, Paul was thoughtful. He glanced at the telegrams, at Everett, and then he said in a flat voice, "Sit down, Ev. Shut the door."

His tone puzzled Everett. He put the telegrams on the desk, sat on the arm of a leather chair. "Yes?"

"Something I'd like to understand," Paul said. "I can see why your uncle would be less than happy about my being here. But why Ben Lork?"

"Oh, nuts, Paul. Now you're getting into office politics."

"What's the low-down?"

"On Ben? Anything I'd say would be a guess."

"I'll buy your guess."

Everett hesitated, glanced at the closed door. Then he said, "Well—of course Ben hopes to be president some day."

"That's understandable. Who wouldn't?"

"Direct line of succession. As long as things go on as they are, Ben's got a damn good chance. If and when my uncle retires or becomes chairman of the Board, Ben could easily step from the controller's job into the presidency. And my uncle would probably back his son-in-law."

Paul nodded.

"But with new management taking over," Everett said, "my uncle *could* lose some degree of—authority. Once the Board gets used to the idea that it doesn't have to follow his leadership, it may not pay too much attention to the present line of succession. That *could* leave Ben out. . . . Mind, all this is a guess."

"I understand. And with Ben out of the picture," Paul asked, "who *would* be the Board's likely choice?"

"Hell, I'm not going to guess about that, too."

"I am," Paul said, leaning back. "You."

Everett shrugged. "Could be."

"Among the other big stockholders your mother would back you. Mark Reickert, too, I imagine."

"It's possible."

"That wouldn't be why *you* wanted new management in, would it?" Paul asked dryly.

Everett said with emphasis, "Listen, pal, I wanted you because I think you can do a job around here that damn well needs to be done!"

Paul looked at the desk lamp. *Same old story,* he thought.

Everybody with his own ax to grind. Always. Everywhere. A sardonic smile flickered about his lips. *Including me.* He slapped both hands down on the arms of his chair and rose. "All right. Let's go get some lunch," he said. "I want to have a look at this co-workers' cafeteria."

Chapter
Five

BACK IN HER STUDIO, on the top floor of the Selby house, Patrice found it hard to concentrate on work. She stood before the easel, in dungarees and a pullover sweater, holding a palette and brushes. She added a highlight to a canvas that was virtually finished, but at the moment neither her mind nor her heart was in the painting.

She was thinking of the quiet way in which her father was concealing how deeply he had been hurt. And she was thinking of the man whose coming had caused the wound.

By instinct and intuition, by sheer perversity perhaps, she had been determined to dislike Paul Blaze. In fairness, however, she had to admit that her dislike was not built on anything he had already done, on anything he had already said. It was built completely on the fact that his presence was a reproach to her father. And that reproach had come from the Board, not from him. Patrice was sensible enough to see that all this was a feeble basis for prejudice against the man. Yet she could not quell it.

When the telephone rang, she welcomed the interruption. She put down the brushes and crossed the room.

"Hi, Pat," a man's voice said. "Warren. How busy are you?"

"Not very. Why?"

Warren Graham said, "The boss is dragging me to that newspaper convention in Washington. Insists I've got to spend the week with him, starting tomorrow. So how about a farewell lunch today? Can you cork up the turpentine?"

Lately Patrice had been seeing Warren Graham once or twice a week. He was one of the few men in Williston whose friendship she really enjoyed. A big, lumbering fellow, he wrote editorials for the *Reporter,* and they were, she thought, the paper's best feature.

"Glad to," she said. "Where and when?"

"One o'clock at Lotti's?"

"Right."

She was grateful to Warren for calling. She wanted to get away from the canvas, from the house, from her thoughts. But escaping thoughts, she quickly discovered, was not easy. Over lunch Warren Graham, too, became aware of her preoccupation.

He looked at her questioningly. "What's eating you, Pat?"

She started; realized she had been silent and absorbed. "Sorry." She quickly resumed eating.

"Trouble?"

"Not really. Just this—change at the store."

"Oh, that. We gave Paul Blaze quite a play on page 3. See it?"

She nodded.

"He sounds like quite a guy," Warren said.

"I wouldn't know."

"Haven't you met him?"

"Briefly. This morning."

Warren smiled. "You don't sound very enthusiastic. But then, you never do—about men."

She looked up sharply. "Why do you say that?"

"Isn't it true?"

"About men in general? Nonsense! I get along well with you, don't I?"

"As long as I keep everything platonic, sure." He spoke with amusement, not with resentment. "But I notice that the instant I try to crack through the romantic barrier, you freeze up. Not very flattering."

She studied him with a feeling of dismay. Was he suggesting that she was frigid? Abnormal in her reactions? The truth was that she had a genuine fondness for Warren Graham. This big, awkward man with his necktie always askew was someone she regarded as a friend. Though he looked more like the foreman of a construction gang than a Ph.D.—he'd got his doctorate at Columbia a couple of years ago—she liked his very awkwardness. That didn't mean she *loved* Warren. . . . Or did it? Patrice was no longer sure about love. Her years of art study in Paris, the miserable affair with Victor de Lange, had left her confused. When and how *could* you be certain about love?

Patrice looked down at her plate. Nobody had ever before suggested that she was frigid. Throughout her teens she had been as gay, as healthily man-conscious as any other girl. She'd had her share of crushes, and she'd enjoyed the excitement of them. Moreover, like other girls, she'd been positive, time after time before her eighteenth birthday, that she *was* deeply in love—only to have the certainty fade as swiftly as it rose.

Her parents had been wise enough, despite the Selby wealth, to send her to Williston's public schools, so that she had grown up on the friendliest of terms with youngsters of all kinds. Emotionally she had in no sense been different from the others. She was sure of that.

But Paris *had* done something to her. No use trying to dodge it.

She was twenty-two when she met Victor de Lange. Old enough to be sure of herself. Old enough to be serious.

He was one of the instructors at the academy—a talented man with blazing black eyes in which Patrice saw only dedication to art. He'd had several exhibitions, successful artistically if not financially, and his work enjoyed the respect of his contemporaries. Tall, lithe, Victor was incredibly good looking; he had the Frenchman's facility of expression, and she was flattered whenever he used it to commend her work.

During her second month in Paris—he had hardly talked to her during the first—Victor asked her to dinner. He took her to the Medici Grill near the Luxembourg Gardens, and afterward they went to the small apartment she had rented in the Rue Vence. He wanted to see the sketches she had been making outside of class.

There was this about Victor: week after week thereafter, sometimes twice a week, he took her to see parts of Paris she had never known existed; he introduced her to his sisters, who had homes in Neuilly; and not once in those weeks did he attempt even a kiss.

By the time he did—the evening he suddenly drew her into his arms, roughly, as though obeying a compulsion—it was as if both had for months been refusing to recognize something inevitable. Patrice knew she loved him. She had loved him from the beginning, and her kiss was as ardent as his.

Victor wanted to marry her at once.

She might have consented, except that she suddenly realized how much her wedding would mean to her father. Surely

Conrad Selby would want to be here. It seemed only fitting to delay until he could arrive. Since the death of his wife he had lived only for his daughters.

So they cabled Williston, and Conrad Selby promised to be in Paris by the first of the month. Patrice's sister Grace would come with him. The wedding was planned for the second. . . .

It was during the period of waiting that Victor was stricken with appendicitis.

Patrice learned about it one morning at the academy, when he failed to appear. She telephoned the concierge of his house to discover that he had been rushed to the hospital at four in the morning.

She caught her breath, then wildly called the hospital. Victor's condition was wholly satisfactory, she was told. No, he would not be allowed visitors this first morning—no one except his wife, who was already with him.

It was a terrible way to learn about Rachelle—like being felled by lightning.

Not that Rachelle *was* his wife. Victor de Lange was not married. It was simply that Rachelle had happened to be with him through that unfortunate night—as, it turned out, she had been with him so many other nights. Rachelle, once a model at the academy, was now unemployed. As she so casually admitted later, she had been "with" Victor a very long time. More than a year. . . .

Patrice turned away from all this with a feeling of sickness. What stunned her was not the fact that Victor had had a mistress—that could be overlooked and forgotten. But how could he, in these last few weeks before the wedding, have this girl spend night after night at his apartment? . . .

It was too late to cable Conrad Selby and Grace not to

to another, talking to buyers, to merchandise managers, to salespeople, Paul began to see half a dozen promotion projects that should and could be launched. Some were simple enough, like jolting the co-workers out of lethargy with a dramatic offer of incentive bonuses. Surely Conrad Selby would assent to this. There was nothing radical in granting such bonuses.

Paul knew, however, that the other ideas he was shaping would demand a revolution in Selby policies. They would certainly carry him into open conflict with the Old Order. The problem was: Ought he to throw the whole program at Conrad Selby at once, like a bombshell?

Why not? he thought. Why not be tough from the start? He'd been hired to run things his way. The sooner he asserted authority, the sooner he could spur Selby's to activity. This was a matter of business. Why allow anyone, including Conrad Selby, to stand in the way?

On the other hand—and the recognition of this factor was a chain on Paul's impulses—Conrad Selby intended to continue as head of the store. They would have to work together for months, for years. To override him at the outset, to rouse his antagonism, could result in endless bickerings, conflicts, feuds, all of which could mean obstruction in the future and a waste of time. . . .

In his hotel rooms Thursday night Paul smoked a dozen cigarettes while he paced the floor, balancing one procedure against another. His tie was loosened and his collar was open. He rubbed uncertain fingers over the back of his neck.

The wise thing to do, he decided, was to suggest something on which they could agree.

Get Selby used to nodding assent. Like gentling an unbroken horse. . . . Once Selby had learned to say yes, it might be easier to win him over to the rest of the initial program.

Psychologically, Paul felt, this would be the sound approach. He decided to adopt it. . . .

Friday morning, when he walked to the store at 9:30, he was ready. He went to the escalators, and there he met Patrice. She was on her way, she said, to the art-goods department on the fourth floor.

Looking at her hatless blond hair, at her straight figure in a beige sports coat, he realized, as the escalator rose, that at their first meeting he hadn't given adequate attention to one outstanding fact: she was an uncommonly attractive girl. He did his best now to be at ease with her.

"Bet you're our most regular art-goods customer," he said.

She tried to match his friendly mood. "As long as Selby's allows me a co-worker's 20 per cent discount, I'll keep buying my paints here."

He remembered something then. "That's a beautiful picture you did for the conference room."

"Like it? Thanks."

"We ought to make more use of you."

"How do you mean?"

"Well, let's see." In a teasing mood, he scratched his cheek. "We could set up an easel in the art-goods department. You could give a public lesson or two. Draw crowds, encourage painting as a hobby, boost the art-goods business."

"If I thought you were serious," she said, "I'd answer that I never put myself on exhibition. Even to boost Selby's volume."

He was still smiling. "Actually, what's wrong with stimulating an interest in art?"

"Not a thing. Except that you don't give a hoot about art, and I do. You're asking me to sell paints and brushes."

"As an artist you object to going into trade, is that it?"
He grinned. "Personally, I have a great respect for trade. Bulwark of the republic. It was industry that saw us through the war—all that sort of thing. Besides, I'm *in* trade."

They were on the third floor now, and as they stepped onto the next escalator Patrice looked up at him curiously. "Mr. Blaze——"

"Your Dad now calls me Paul."

"Seriously. *Do* you see people that way? As—human gimmicks for sales promotion?"

"Only when they have something the store can use. As to this art-goods notion, the more I think of it, the better I——"

"Forget it. *I* won't be a gimmick."

She sounded annoyed to an unreasonable degree. Why she should show displeasure over something so trivial, Paul could not understand. But they were at the fourth floor now, where she would leave him, and he made no issue of the matter.

She said good-by. He watched her walk off as the escalator carried him to the next floor. Nice figure, he mused; very nice legs. Matter of fact, she was most attractive. But touchy. Very touchy.

He dismissed the whole thing. There was the sales promotion program to take up with Conrad Selby, and that was far more important. . . .

An hour later, in his office, Selby listened with interest. "Institutional ads?" he repeated. "What kind?"

"Half-pages twice a week," Paul said. "We'll call the series 'Inside Selby's.' Written by a pro, of course. They've got to read like magazine pieces. The idea is to play up Selby services in an interesting way. We'll start with 'Ella Bly.' That department can use a boost."

Ella Bly was the name Selby's had adopted for its mail

order and personal shopping service. The department was managed by Mrs. Helen Wood Heinemann who had three young women as assistants. To shop by letter, by telephone, or to seek special help within the store, you simply asked for Miss Ella Bly, and one of the women came to your aid.

"Here's a rough idea of what I have in mind," Paul said. "The first piece should touch on these main points and illustrations." He passed a sheet of notes across the desk.

Putting on horn-rimmed glasses, Conrad Selby picked up the paper and read:

1. Last year a Williston newlywed couple went to live in Puerto Rico. Asked Ella Bly, by mail, to furnish their San Juan home. Six rooms. Left all details to her on a $4,500 budget. She did the whole job from Selby's for $4,200.

2. People sick at home or in hospitals constantly call on Ella Bly to buy their needs.

3. Soldiers and civilians overseas send Ella Bly Christmas lists, plus checks, and rely on her to choose and send all their gifts.

4. People in a hurry stop in the store to give Ella Bly their shopping lists, and she does everything.

5. Point out that we are proud of Ella Bly because through her customers all over the world express *confidence* in Selby's.

6. Wind up with point that you, too—whether you need a handkerchief or a completely furnished home—can call on Ella Bly for free services.

Selby nodded his gray head judiciously. "It *could* be good."

Paul went on, "Other articles in the series will feature the rest of our free services: interior decorators, bridal consultant, free fashion shows for women's clubs, and so on. Then a series on 'How to Buy.' Interviews with our buyers and merchandise managers on what inside information to know when choosing china, silver, furniture—anything you can find in Selby's."

"It sounds like an excellent idea. What will all this cost?"

"Two half-pages a week, plus the fee of a writer."

Conrad Selby did not actually say the plan pleased him because it was dignified; reassured him because it avoided the circus-barker type of publicity he had dreaded. Yet Paul could almost see the relief running through his mind.

Selby said, "Certainly we can give it a try. Found a writer?"

"There's a fellow named Warren Graham I was told about. Writes editorials for the *Reporter*—good ones—and free lances on the side. Did some magazine articles."

"Graham's all right," Selby agreed with a nod. "Friend of Patrice's."

Lighting a cigarette, Paul did some quick thinking. This matter of institutional ads had gone more smoothly than he had anticipated. Why not, then, push a bit further? Make the most of this opportunity.

"On the question of *direct* sales promotion," he said. "I want to get going on that, too."

Selby leaned back, took off his glasses. "What do you have in mind?"

"To begin with, special daily sales. In at least two or three departments every day of the week. Make *every* day a big sale day at Selby's. We'll need two additional pages of advertising every morning to put the campaign over."

Now he could see Selby stiffen. The president drummed on the edge of the desk. "That would turn us into a six-floor bargain basement."

"Not at all. Two or three specials a day—out of all our departments—won't turn us into a bargain basement."

Selby drew a long breath, then pressed the button on his desk. "I'd like Ben in on this," he said. His face had become grave. When Maud Heller appeared, he asked her to call Mr. Lork, and presently the controller joined them.

"Paul has a plan," Selby said. He seemed to be forcing himself to sound impartial. His voice never left its low pitch. "It calls for daily sales. He wants to spot them around the store. And give them two full-page ads every morning—in addition to our present advertising schedule."

The controller seemed puzzled when he turned to Paul. "You mean daily loss leaders? The old come-on game?"

"No," Paul said. "Legitimate sales at legitimate mark-downs. On specials we'll buy at discount specially *for* these sales. If you want to call them come-ons in the sense that they'll bring people to the store, okay. That's the object—to attract crowds every day of the week."

Selby was shaking his head. He had made up his mind. "Sorry, Paul. I can't go for that."

"Why?"

"Bound to destroy quality standards."

"I don't see——"

"To buy at discounts every day of the week, to find enough low-priced merchandise to keep us going on such a campaign, we'd have to hunt for manufacturers' canceled orders, left-overs, distress goods, damaged goods, seconds, irregulars——"

"Hold it," Paul said. "Canceled orders, yes. Overstock, yes. But not seconds, nothing damaged. We don't have to let down on *quality*." He was too restless now to sit still. He walked about the office, and the lines of his jaws were sharp. "Plenty of manufacturers have good canceled merchandise on

was a direct challenge, and they both knew it. Selby rose, pushed his hands into his pockets, went to look out of the window.

"Paul, I'm not in the habit of calling special Board meetings for every decision I have to make."

"Isn't this a decision the Board has to make?"

"Not at all."

"Now wait—let me get this straight. It's my impression I'm here to get a full-fledged sales promotion program under way. I believe that's what the Board hired me to do. If I'm wrong, let's find out."

"Very well. There will be a regular monthly meeting of the Board in two weeks."

"Why waste two weeks?"

Suddenly Conrad Selby turned from the window. He could no longer hide his anger. It flared in his eyes.

"What are you trying to do, Paul?" His voice was still quiet. "Insist on a showdown between us?"

"I don't like to put it that way. On the other hand——"

"On the other hand, maybe you're right. Maybe we *should* have a showdown. If I'm no longer making decisions at Selby's, it might be a good thing to find out at once. . . . Yes. I'll call a special meeting of the Board for Monday afternoon!"

Chapter

Seven

THOUGH HE HAD WON his point, Paul left Conrad Selby with a sense of dissatisfaction. Somehow, he felt, he had lost control of the situation; it was Selby who had made the final positive decision concerning the Board meeting. Worse, he had made it in anger.

This first discussion of plans should not have been allowed to become a dispute. That had been a mistake involving poor judgment, poor psychology, bad business. Paul knew he had pressed too hard. What he had won was a Pyrrhic victory, and he was irritated with himself.

The unpleasant feeling persisted through the morning, while he made rounds of the upper three floors; persisted through lunch, to which he took the head of personnel, Mrs. Isabelle Rorich, in order to get a briefing in co-worker problems. Late in the afternoon, returning from a conference with the basement manager, Paul found a memo from Maud Heller on his desk:

Bernardine Sorel, it said, had twice tried to reach him; could he get in touch with her?

He went down to the fashion floor where he found Bernardine in the dress department, checking stock. In the perfection of her appearance she always reminded him of a model about to have her picture snapped; the bronze-colored hair invariably looked as if it had been set five minutes ago.

He asked, "What's on your mind, Berry?"

She glanced around with some uneasiness, then suggested, "Can you come to my office?"

Behind the partition he followed her to the cubicle that contained her desk, racks of sample dresses, a lingering scent of Oriental perfume. Colored fashion illustrations, clipped from magazines, covered the walls.

Here Bernardine faced him with visible anxiety. "Paul, Mr. Selby has sent out notices for this special Board meeting. Apparently he feels you're going in for a wild splurge of advertising."

"Is that the way he put it?"

"Well, that was the inference."

"He's wrong."

"Anyhow, during lunch I talked to seven of the Board members." Bernardine spoke quickly, as though she feared interruption. "Paul, nobody wants to see him *humiliated* again. Nobody wants to see him get another kick in the teeth by an adverse vote. He may be slow in some things, but we really like Conrad Selby. If there's any way of avoiding this embarrassment of a vote——" She paused. "I'm sure the Board *wants* action, and the majority will support you, all right—except, maybe, for Randolph Green. But——"

"What's the matter with Randolph Green?"

"Don't ask me. His thoughts are his own. I just *think* he'll go along with Selby; I may be wrong. . . . But about this meeting. Is there any way to avoid it?"

"Only if I throw my weight around. Only if I issue orders without Selby's approval."

Bernardine looked at the profusion of papers on the desk. "It—it might almost be better that way," she said in a low voice.

"Sure. That way he hates only me. Nobody on the Board has to take the onus. Is that it?"

"Frankly, yes. I wish you'd think about it, Paul."

He said, "Look, Berry. I consulted Selby because I don't want him to feel I'm ignoring him right from the start, pushing him aside. I want him to feel he's still boss."

"I understand. Everybody understands. But isn't there any way you can put off this business of a showdown? It'll be painful and bad for everybody. Bound to make things around here worse than they are."

After a moment he patted her arm and turned away. "I'll see what I can do."

Back in his own office Paul reconsidered the situation. Like the others, he certainly had no desire to see Conrad Selby humiliated. For one thing, it would not be easy to work with a man who felt persecuted, hounded, repeatedly let down by those who owed him loyalty. A man hurt like that would constantly be trying to hit back. Perhaps there *was* a way to avoid all this. . . .

He thought of it until after five, and as the closing gong sounded he went into the president's office. Only Maud Heller was there, gathering papers.

"Mr. Selby just went home," she said. "Sorry."

Paul waited a half-hour to allow the president to reach his house, then telephoned. It was Patrice who answered. Her father, she said, had not yet arrived.

Paul told her, "I'd like to see him tonight. Think he could spare an hour?"

"As far as I know, he's staying in. Ben and my sister Grace are coming for dinner. Why don't you come over?"

"I'll drop by about nine," Paul said. "Thanks."

When he drove to the white hilltop house that evening, he found the family in the living room. They were having after-dinner coffee, and a record player was halfway through the Brahms "Academic Festival Overture." While listening, Ben Lork had been setting up the ivory pieces of a chess set, and Paul wondered in surprise if the family habitually spent evenings like this. He sat down, uncomfortably sensitive about being an outsider; feeling, too, that the discussion he had come for would be ill-timed. Yet he could hardly back away from it now.

Patrice, smiling, brought him coffee. "Or would you like something stronger?" she asked.

"Thanks, no. Coffee's fine."

She wore a casual pale-blue dress with a gay kerchief and pin at the neck. Paul liked the combination. There was individuality in the way she bore herself, just as there was individuality in the way she painted. It seemed a pity, he thought, that this girl, like her father, threatened to be difficult to get along with. . . .

Her older sister seemed far more friendly. A dark-haired woman of thirty, almost as tall as her father, Grace Lork had a cordial smile, and, he suspected, an instinctive liking for people. There was a glint of humor in her eyes, as though she took few things seriously.

If the family was curious about his reason for coming, they gave no indication of it. Nor did Conrad Selby allow himself to show any angry remembrance of the morning's dispute.

"Personally," he said to Ben when the Overture ended, "I prefer the Koussevitzky version." He went to the record player, and Paul gathered there had been some artistic disagreement on this recording. "It has more brilliance, more lightness, more humor."

"But in this Walter record," Ben argued, "you get a sense of depth, of power, that I miss in the Koussevitzky."

"Matter of personal taste."

Grace, laughing, said to Paul, "Hope you don't mind our musical squabbles. Ben and Dad have been at it for years. They never get anywhere, but they must find it fun to disagree."

Paul wasn't accustomed to evenings like this. What did these people do, he wondered—drop all thoughts of the store when they came home? Start a new life? For himself, he could seldom forget his job. It lived with him. Its tensions kept his nerves twanging.

Maybe the answer was that when you'd had comfort and security all your life you could *afford* to forget the struggle for them. You could turn your mind in other directions.

Lighting his pipe, Ben said, "I'm sure Paul didn't come to discuss our musical preferences."

"No, of course not." Selby looked at Paul questioningly. "Something on your mind?"

"We-ll, about this Board meeting."

"Oh?" Selby made no suggestion of going to another room for a private discussion. Paul glanced around. They were all watching him now, curious, expectant. He decided to plunge.

"Seems to me such a meeting could establish a bad precedent," he said to Selby. "Do we really have to run to the Board every time we don't see eye to eye? Especially in a matter we can settle so easily?"

Selby asked, "How do you mean?"

"Why don't we give the program a month's try? That's not much of a gamble. If it doesn't pay off in a month—fine, we'll ditch it. If it *is* paying by then, you probably won't want to stop it. We don't need a vote of the Board for a trial run."

He waited, watching Conrad Selby's face. The gray-haired man sipped his cognac. On the couch Patrice, with her feet tucked under her skirt, glanced from Paul to her father.

Ben Lork promptly said, "Good idea. Makes sense that way."

It seemed to Paul that he had found the only way to salvage both his program and Selby's pride, and everybody knew it. There was ample time to cancel the Board meeting.

"Sounds to me, Dad," Grace put in, "like a very sensible compromise."

Selby put down his glass. His manner was firm.

"Paul," he said, "apparently I haven't made myself clear. I don't believe in spending money we haven't yet earned. That goes for spending it over a year or over a month or over a day. The *principle* is wrong. I can't compromise on what I believe to be wrong."

Paul said, "Look. Suppose Selby's were a new store about to start in business. Would you say we ought not to advertise, we ought not to spend a cent on promotion, till we see how much is coming in?"

"There's no analogy. In a case like that promotion funds would be part of a calculated investment, like the cost of merchandise. What you're proposing is entirely different—an out-and-out promotional gamble." Selby shook his head. "Paul, I happen also to be a director of the Williston Bank. I would never in good conscience vote to let the bank spend funds it hadn't earned. Why should I be less careful about my own business?"

"But in one short month——"

"If it's wrong, it's wrong. Even for a month. When the

Board votes, I think you'll find we're more conservative, more level-headed, than you suspect. We're just not a gambling crowd—never have been—especially when the gamble could wipe out a year's dividends."

There was no swaying the man. At the beginning Paul had some help from Ben, but Selby's son-in-law must have known the futility of arguing against the old man's principles, and he soon gave up the attempt. Paul kept at it alone.

"What it comes down to," he said, "is this: You want to let the size of last year's volume dictate this year's activities."

"Not activities," Selby corrected. *"Expenditures."*

"It amounts to the same thing. You can't have one without the other. My point is that if we're going to get ahead, we can't allow last year's business to keep us constricted, like a strait jacket. We've got to be free to exploit this year for all it's worth."

"I'm not sure I agree with your use of the term strait jacket," Selby said. "On the other hand, I do agree that our points of view—our fundamental philosophies in this matter— are completely opposed. I can't turn my back on my convictions, Paul."

"Neither can I."

Paul spoke tautly. Facing Conrad Selby's inflexible sense of rightness, he could appreciate and admire the man's integrity. But then, was his own integrity less solid? He was not attempting tricks; he was not even concerned, at the moment, with the size of his own bonus. He felt honestly dedicated to the job of increasing the store's business, and he was offering a plan which he believed to be good, productive, and intelligent.

Strangely, though he was irritated by Selby's opposition, Paul had to respect it. In some inscrutable way he even liked the man for his refusal to change his standards. But at the moment this reflection was no help to the store.

"Please don't misunderstand," Selby said. "I have deep respect for your energy and your determination. And I'd be a fool if I didn't applaud your hope of increasing the store's volume. But as for your methods—Paul, I'm sorry. I can't go along."

"That gets us nowhere."

"I wasn't planning to go anywhere—along this route."

By ten-thirty Paul had to abandon the hope. "All right," he said bitterly, "then we'll have to let the Board decide. . . . Sorry I barged into your evening like this."

When he left it was with a sense of defeat. You tried to save a man from being hurt, and he brushed you off. What could you do?

Patrice saw him to the door, even walked out on the wide porch with him. The night was warm, with a full moon overhead. Paul looked out over the long valley in which Williston lay. It's distant neon brightness glowed against the sky.

The girl beside him said, "You needn't be so annoyed. Dad can't back something he doesn't believe in."

"All I'm trying to do," Paul answered, "is save him from another clash with the Board."

"Then why don't you take the obvious way?"

"What way?"

"Withdraw the plan."

He turned to her in growing exasperation. Patrice's eyes were almost squinting, as though she were studying his face as a subject of a painting. He said, "Look, I've told you before. I'm being paid to put ideas into *action!*"

"But do you have to push this particular idea? You must

have a hundred others—the kind Dad could go along with. Why not try the others first?"

"Temporize? Where will that get the store?"

"I think once you've shown an actual increase in business, Dad will feel differently about spending money. It's all a matter of timing."

"I can't deliberately put off a program that's bound to produce business quicker than anything else we could do. There's too much at stake."

In the moonlight he saw a smile come to Patrice's lips— a cynical, almost weary smile. She looked toward the lights of Williston. "I forgot how much was at stake," she whispered. "A block of stock. Of course."

It hit Paul like a slap. Anger flared in him, and he had an impulse to seize this girl, to shake her, to hurt her as she had hurt him. His lean face became taut.

"That's a hell of a thing to say."

"Why can't we be frank?" she asked. "Are you really interested in saving Dad from being hurt? Aren't you just trying to make things easier for yourself?"

This time, to her astonishment, he did grasp her arms. He forced her to face him, to see the wrath in his eyes. He said, "What the devil's the matter with you people? It's *your* business I'm trying to build!"

She was silent, obviously surprised by the grip on her arms.

"Okay, so I do want something for myself!" he said. "What's wrong about that? I'm not asking for anything I don't earn!"

"Please let me go."

"I'll put this deal over in *spite* of your father! I tried *not* to ride over him, not to throw my weight around. But he won't have it that way! All right, then. We'll do it his way!"

He released her then. He went down the porch steps and got into his car and slammed the door. You tried to be decent, and they slapped you down. . . .

"Good night," she said.

"Good night!"

As he drove away he had a strange flash of recollection. He saw the sardonic features of Edmond C. Christie, remembered Christie's cynical prediction that the only way to get a real hold on an enterprise like Selby's was to marry into it. That was bitterly funny now. Paul uttered a derisive laugh. Marriage into *this* stubborn crowd, he thought, would be too much to pay even for the complete ownership of Selby's. . . .

Chapter

Eight

On Saturday evening Martha was worried. She sat in the bedroom of her Williston Heights house, the telephone at her ear. This was the fifth time she had tried to reach New York. She glanced at the cloisonné clock on the vanity table. It was almost 8:30.

"Sorry, ma'am," the long distance operator said. "The number doesn't answer."

"Will you keep trying, please?"

"Yes, ma'am. In twenty minutes."

Martha Selby went to the mirror, nervously fluffing up the waves of her graying hair. This evening she wore an amethyst hostess gown that made her seem all the more statuesque, its long chiffon skirt swirling with every move she made. Looking at her reflection, she wondered if she really appeared to be fifty. She doubted it. Anyhow, Jerry Weed didn't seem to think so. . . .

She looked again at the clock. In a few minutes Dr. Philip Selby and Mark Reickert would arrive, and her son Everett. If only she could have Jerry's call completed before they came.

As she went down the stairs she thought in anxiety about the special Board meeting Conrad Selby had summoned. It had seemed a nuisance, interfering with her plans for a trip to New York. She had protested—until Conrad had explained why it was necessary. Now she hardly knew what to think.

Despite the fact that she had so flagrantly opposed him at recent Board meetings, she had a deep respect for Conrad. She liked him as a person; admired his staunchness in maintaining his principles, his standards, his beliefs. The fact that she could not always agree with him was unfortunate, but it could not make her deny Conrad's essential integrity.

There had been a time, not many years ago, when she had invariably followed his business advice. At Board meetings she had almost blindly voted his way. His methods were never spectacular, but under his presidency she had never missed a dividend.

Now, as she sat down in the living room to await her guests, Martha remembered odd moments in her relationship with Conrad. They came to trouble her conscience. She re- called how, when her husband had died, he had quietly and competently helped her to rearrange her life; how he had su- pervised the legalities of turning her husband's estate over to her own name. At that time Mark Reickert had offered to buy a good part of her holdings—"In case you need the cash," he had said—but Conrad had opposed the sale. She had accepted Conrad's advice and she had never regretted it. Cash from Mark might have been spent long ago; stock kept her income steady and reliable.

In his own way, she had to concede, Conrad had built patiently but well. She could, for instance, remember every detail of the celebration that had marked the remodeling of the Selby store. It had been a half-million dollar project. At the dinner which climaxed its completion Conrad had made a characteristically restrained speech; he had finished by saying,

"If I sound proud, I know you will forgive me. All of us have reason to be proud. We have built soundly, and what we see here is a monument to our co-operation."

Sometimes, in the depths of her mind, Martha was ashamed of the disloyalty she had lately shown her brother-in-law. But she couldn't help it. She needed money—far more than the store was yielding. Wasn't the whole point of running a business to make it earn its maximum potential? She tried to appease herself by thinking that Conrad—much as she admired him—had, in these late years, lost the spark of enterprise. You could not expect a man of sixty-two to have the energy of somebody half his age. In justice to everyone who relied on the Selby store, co-workers as well as stockholders, it *had* to be made more profitable.

But Martha knew, with a pang that distressed her, that all this was rationalization. What had really turned her against Conrad was this need for money. To be more accurate, it was Jerry Weed's need for money. She couldn't let Jerry down. She couldn't turn her back on something which had come to mean so much to her. . . .

The doorbell sounded, snatching her out of the reverie. Martha rose, instinctively adjusting her hair, and tried to thrust the disturbing thoughts aside.

Mark Reickert and Dr. Philip Selby arrived together; Everett came a few minutes later.

"For heaven's sake, Mibs," her son said, kissing her cheek, "what's the emergency?"

"The Board meeting." She took Everett to the others in the living room. Mark, heavy-set and bald, was already pouring highballs. Dr. Selby had settled in a wing chair where he was comfortably filling a pipe. A slight man with good-humored eyes, he had pepper-colored hair graying at the temples. At forty-eight Philip was the family bachelor. He viewed the rest of the clan with amusement, as though eternally entertained by the devious and unpredictable involvements of family life.

"Did Conrad tell all of you the reasons for this meeting?" Martha asked as she sat down.

Mark Reickert said, "Con's trying to obstruct something."

"Well, *I'm* a bit scared," Martha confessed.

Dr. Philip Selby, as he lit his pipe, sent a quizzical glance at the tall woman who was his cousin. "Just what's bothering you, Martha? You're not the worrying kind."

"According to Con, Paul's planning a program that may cost us several hundred thousand dollars."

"So?"

"Suppose Paul does *not* produce a two-million-dollar increase. Suppose he's being over-optimistic. That kind of spending would cut deep into dividends."

Everett said, "Mibs, that kind of spending, as you call it, isn't really spending at all. It's promotion. Dollars that come back with more dollars in tow."

Philip smiled at the bowl of his pipe. "Martha, you surprise me. You *asked* for Paul Blaze. You asked for everything that's happening—and now you're the first to waver!"

"Aren't you worried?"

"Not a bit."

"Well, Phil," Martha said, "*you* can afford to be calm—with your doctor's income, your real estate income. All I've got to count on is my dividends from the store."

"You'll get them."

Mark Reickert gestured with the hand that held his highball, almost spilling it, "Martha, we're the ones who put Paul Blaze in. If we don't back him, who will?"

"Just a moment," Philip said. "Correction. 'We' are not the ones who put Paul Blaze in. I voted against hiring him. But now that he is in, I'd consider it foolish not to let him work out his plans."

There was silence. They all stared at Philip. Finally Martha leaned forward. *"You did not vote for him, Phil?"*

"No. Didn't want to break Con's heart." Philip puffed at his pipe. "But since the Board did vote that way, we may as well make the best of it. This time I'll support Blaze." He took the pipe from his mouth, looked at it. "I hope, though, another vote against him won't persuade Con to pull out."

"Pull out?" Mark Reickert laughed with scorn. "Don't be silly. Not Con!"

"He *might* resign, you know," Philip said thoughtfully. "He's always had his own way before this."

Mark said, "It would be the worst thing that could happen. And he knows it."

"Why do you, of all people, say that?" Philip sent him an oblique look. "Thought *you* considered Con too conservative."

"I'm just being realistic," Mark said. "Williston people back the town's old families. Local pride. If they once got the idea that Con Selby had been forced out by this new management, they'd be thumbs down on new management—especially new management that horns in from out of town. Be the worst kind of reaction."

Everett suddenly rose. He crossed the room to refill his glass. "This is ridiculous," he said. "No need to worry about Uncle Con's resigning. Ben won't let him. You know perfectly well Ben wants him there for protective reasons. You can't inherit a presidency from a man who isn't president."

At this Philip gave Everett an amused look. Martha, however, saw nothing funny in it. She still could not escape her primary doubt. "Do you think there's any real chance Paul may fail? That this added advertising expenditure *could* be wasted?"

Everett said, "Oh, Mibs, stop worrying! Paul knows what he's doing."

"Can't make money unless you spend money," Mark asserted. "This thing'll work out fine. Bound to. We've got to vote for it."

The telephone rang.

Martha rose quickly, went to the foyer in a swirl of amethyst chiffon. When she picked up the telephone, the operator said, "Ready with your call to New York."

She caught her breath. "Oh. Hold it, please. I'll take it on another extension." She glanced into the living room. "Excuse me, won't you? Be right down."

She hurried upstairs to take the call in her bedroom, behind a closed door. Sitting on the edge of the bed, she kept her voice low: "Jerry?"

"Hello, angel," a deep voice said.

"Been trying to reach you all afternoon!"

"Sorry. I was out—trying to make this damn third act click in my head. . . . Coming Monday?"

"Jerry, I can't! There's an emergency Board meeting——"

"Oh, hell, not *that* again!"

"Jerry, please. You know how much it can mean to us."

"I was looking forward to seeing you Monday."

"I'll make it Tuesday."

"And stay a while?"

She uttered a nervous laugh. "If you like. A few days."

"Still don't want me to come to Williston?"

"No, Jerry, no. Please."

He laughed. "Well, you know best. Tuesday, then, angel?"

"Tuesday," Martha promised. . . .

She hung up presently, sitting still, waiting for her nerves to uncoil. Why was it she still became tense whenever she talked to Jerry Weed? And why couldn't he ever understand the awkwardness of his coming to Williston? The inevitable effect on her family, her friends. . . . It would have been different, of course, if Jerry were—say a man of fifty-five. Even fifty. Her own age. But Jerry was not quite thirty-nine. Williston, in its intolerance, simply wouldn't understand a thing like that, how wonderful it made a woman feel, how young and desired and alive, to be loved, to be called beautiful, by a younger man. . . .

At the mirror Martha hastily used her lipstick. As she looked at her flushed reflection she thought about Jerry's play. She was proud of him. Why no producer had so far jumped at it, she didn't know. Such disinterest seemed inconceivable. Especially, as Jerry said, when the play could be put on for only eighty thousand dollars. Five characters and a single set. . . . Well, if Selby's stock skyrocketed, eighty thousand dollars wouldn't be difficult to raise.

Martha turned away from the mirror. She looked very attractive now, eyes bright, lips smiling, as she hurried down the stairs. She wondered why she had even hesitated about supporting Paul Blaze's plans. Everything—*everything*—depended on a boom in the stock of the Selby Department Store. As Mark said, you had to spend money to make money.

An hour later Mark Reickert, behind the wheel of his black car, drove away from Martha's home with a smile. When he relaxed like this, enjoying his thoughts, his face settled down into amiable bulges of fat.

It was an hour's drive to his home in Medill—to the big brick house he'd built for Emily two years before her death. The way ran over hills and through farmlands that smelled this moonlit night of wet loam and fertilizer. There was a smooth, four-lane highway, and he didn't mind the drive at all. In fact, Mark found pleasure in his cigar, in the mild spring evening, in everything that was happening at the Selby store.

Maybe it would be hard on Conrad's pride, he mused, to have Paul Blaze elbow him aside. But what of it? High time Conrad was kicked out of his complacency. Conrad and his dignity. His goddam, stiff-necked dignity. Mark laughed at it.

Not that he had any illusions about his own standing in Conrad's eyes. It had been the same for thirty years. Conrad, he knew, considered him crude, uneducated, rough as a gorilla —an outsider who'd crashed into the family by force.

Sure, it had been by force. Their own goddam fault. Why did they have to set up such a stinking howl when he'd wanted to marry Emily? So he had never gone to college. So he had worked for a packing house at the time. What kind of crime was it to deal in meat? Why was it lower than dealing in dry goods? In furniture? Anything wrong with the Cudahys, the Armours, the Swifts? Those boys could buy out the Selbys a hundred times over!

And yet the family had objected to Emily's marrying "a butcher." Some joke, all right. Mark grunted every time he remembered the satisfaction he'd had in rubbing the family's nose in it. He had taken Emily to Pittsburgh and he'd wired back: "Emily and I married this afternoon. Very happy. Both love meat."

Of course, Conrad Selby, the dean of the family, had

never forgiven him—he was sure of that. But Conrad hadn't been able to do anything about it. Emily had inherited her own block of Selby stock—the stock that was now Mark's. She'd have collected her dividends even if she had married an African head-hunter. Before the days of high taxes they had been fairly sizable dividends, too—big enough to help Mark establish his chain of restaurants.

He took the cigar from his mouth, held it out of the window to let the ashes blow away, put it back between his teeth. He was no more ashamed of having been "a butcher" than of operating restaurants. What he *couldn't* take—what he'd never be able to take as long as he lived—was Conrad's air of superiority. It got under his skin every time they were together. Conrad with his church-deacon manner. . . .

Well, circumstances were changing now. At last. Smartest thing he'd ever done, Mark reflected, was fight to bring Paul Blaze into the store.

Larger volume? Bigger dividends? Sure. That was fine. A man had to be crazy not to enjoy the prospect of earning more money. But there would be something else, too, and Mark looked forward to it with relish as to a vindication of his whole life.

Tonight he had opposed the idea of Conrad's resignation. Bad public relations, he'd said. But that wouldn't be true in a year. In a year Williston would have accepted the store's new management. Nobody would give much attention to the fact that Conrad Selby, in his sixties, had decided to retire.

No, in a year Mark wouldn't for a minute oppose the idea of Conrad's resigning. In fact, it would be perfect if it could be arranged, encouraged, precipitated. . . .

And after that? Between himself and Martha—and maybe with the support of Philip—they could vote Everett into the presidency. It shouldn't be hard. Mark felt confident he could manage things. Well enough, at any rate, to have himself elected Chairman of the Board.

That was what he wanted. To be Chairman of the Board.

He could see Conrad's face when it happened. The butcher. The guy nobody had wanted in the family. Sitting as Chairman of the Board of the Selby Department Store. . . .

Mark chuckled.

Dr. Philip Selby reached his home in an uncomfortable mood. It was a small white house to which an extension had been built for his office suite. Now, just before midnight, the extension was dark, but a light shone in the living room. The couple who kept house for the doctor, Ed and Minnie Jackson, always left a light when he was out.

In the living room he filled a calabash pipe, then sat down in the chair where he liked to read. This evening, however, he didn't open a book. He smoked and contemplated the empty fireplace.

One thing lingered in his mind as a result of the conversation at Martha's home: Everett's comment about Ben Lork's ambition to be the store's president.

Philip sucked thoughtfully at the pipe.

All his life he had been close to the store, in spite of the fact that he had never worked in it. His family had groaned at his decision to study medicine. No doubt they had hoped that he, too, would go into Selby's. But he liked medicine. He had done well at it. Indeed, no doctor in Williston had a better general practice. Yet the store had always been close to Philip's heart; and when he had inherited from his father the stock which carried him to a seat on the Board of Directors, he had known that this must henceforth be a major interest in his life.

It was. He wondered now, with some uneasiness, what choice he *would* make when it became necessary to vote for either Everett or Ben as the next president.

The trouble was that he liked them both.

Everett, of course, was blood kin. He had known Everett since the day of his birth. He used to go to high school games to watch Everett play football and basketball and baseball, and Philip used to take an almost possessive pride in Everett's skill. Even now he liked to play golf with the young giant. It gave him a secret sense of pride to be beaten by one of the new Selby generation who could shoot a 77.

Moreover, he approved of Everett's choice of a wife, Betty, who had charm and humor and verve; and he was fond of Everett's two children. Finally, there was no doubt that Everett Selby did an energetic and efficient job at the store. The boy *could* make a vigorous president.

But couldn't Ben Lork, too?

Ben, Philip reflected as he smoked, was by temperament more serious than Everett. Quietly competent, he knew everything there was to know about Selby's. Nobody—not even Conrad himself—could give more detailed information about the store's operations. Ben was level-headed and able without being spectacular.

The fact that he had not been born a Selby ought not to be considered at all, Philip felt. Ben had come from a well-to-do family that had for decades operated textile mills. The mills had been sold while Ben was in the army, so that he'd had no family enterprise of his own to enter. He was, however, the son of comfortable wealth. His marriage to Grace had been, in every sense, a marriage of two people in equal social and financial brackets.

Philip had always thought that Grace had made the perfect choice of a husband for herself. The Lorks had a good family life. Their two red-headed girls were one of Philip's delights. In truth, they made him wonder, in moments of introspection, whether he had been wise never to marry. Years ago —when he had been under thirty—Philip had once been within two weeks of marriage. He had been deeply in love with Lucy Arnold; and when a truck had shattered her body as it had shattered her car, killing her instantly, it had shattered something in Philip Selby, too.

Now he was content to spend the rest of his life alone. He had simple tastes—golf, music, books, bridge. And he enjoyed playing bridge with Ben as much as he enjoyed golf with Everett. Characteristically, Ben was one of the best bridge players in Williston—primarily because he never played a card before first studying all its possibilities.

As to making a choice between the two men for the presidency of the store, however——

Philip smoked and meditated for a long time.

He supposed, all things considered, that Ben would be the better president. Ben was more mature, older. He had more business experience, more general knowledge of the store. Though he was never the hail-fellow-well-met that Everett was, you had to respect his quiet judgment. It seemed to Philip that, confronted with the choice, he *would* probably vote for Ben. . . .

Yet he wasn't sure. He rose, sighing, and went to knock out the ashes of the pipe in the fireplace. If only either Ben or Everett had something of Paul Blaze's flair for creating new

ideas. . . . If only one of them could whip the store into the
activity that Blaze managed to produce. . . .

He put out the light and went up to the bedroom. Why
he was so disturbed, Philip couldn't understand. After all, he
had a pleasant life of his own: the practice of medicine; free
evenings to devote to his friends—and he was socially a popular
figure in Williston. Yes, he had much to enjoy. Why worry
about who the next president of Selby's might be?

He had only one real and immediate concern about the
store, and that was to save Conrad Selby from exposing himself to a series of humiliating defeats. He liked Conrad too well
to see him hurt. He wished there were some way of persuading
Conrad to give Paul Blaze his head for a while, without arguing about and opposing every innovation. But how to accomplish this, Philip didn't know. For the present he'd simply have
to use his own voting power on the Board honestly, as events
dictated from day to day.

But he went to bed with the uneasy feeling that he had
found an ailment for which he knew no treatment.

Chapter
Nine

ON MONDAY the plan to run daily sales, supported by an all-out advertising campaign, won the overwhelming approval of the Board of Directors. But when it was all over, Paul walked out of the conference room without any sense of triumph. All he could feel was exasperation with Selby's stubbornness in forcing the issue. Surely, he thought as he went down the corridor, there was nothing for which he could blame himself. He had made every reasonable effort to avoid a crisis, every possible concession short of surrender. What more could he have done?

Still, he had been stung at the meeting by Selby's drawn look. Sitting in his own office now, tapping a pencil on the desk, Paul tried to shake off emotionalism. This was business. He reminded himself that he was here for one purpose only: to increase the store's receipts this year by more than $1,000,000. And if anyone offered obstructions, they had to be overcome. It was the only way to justify his position. He couldn't afford sentimentalism. It merely complicated matters.

He rang for Maud Heller. "I want all buyers and merchandise managers to meet me in the conference room at four-thirty," he told her. "And ask Donald Ripley to see me first thing in the morning." Donald Ripley was in charge of display.

An hour later Paul faced some thirty of the store's executives. He stood at the head of the long conference table, a trim, taut figure in a smoothly tailored gray suit. After he had explained the daily special project, he made his instructions brief. What he wanted was an immediate search of all markets for goods that could be bought at special prices.

"That goes for every department in the store," he said. "We're out for specials. If you have any doubts about a buy, call Mr. Lork or me." Then he added, "Another thing: As soon as we work out the details we'll announce a new incentive bonus system. We want you—*all* the co-workers—to share in whatever added business we produce."

He could feel a stir. He could see they were interested.

But there was skepticism, too. Sam Taber, the head furniture buyer, said in his laconic way, "I know where I can buy low-priced furniture in a hurry, all right. Only, it's borax."

"Borax is out!" Paul said. "No inferior stuff—and that goes for everybody. We buy top grade merchandise or nothing."

More questions came. As they multiplied he could feel the steady rise of excitement among these people. He had hoped his own enthusiasm would infuse them all, and it was happening that way. . . .

The meeting ended at five-fifteen. When it was over he took Randolph Green and Bernardine to his office. A familiar tightness had caught his stomach.

"Fashions," he told Green, "will have to be the backbone of this daily special operation. I want fashion specials as often as we can get them. Coats, suits, dresses, blouses, everything. One a day if possible."

Green, however, seemed uneasy about the idea. He was the

only buyer who had appeared disturbed at the meeting. "It's going to be tough, Mr. Blaze," he said. "Covering a market of four thousand firms takes time and more manpower than we've got."

"Hire extra buyers. Promote some of your own people."

But Green still frowned. His dark hair, parted in the middle, had become rumpled. He put two fingers into his vest pocket. "What—what about our regular lines? While we run these specials, do we stock the same basic inventory as in the past?"

"Sure. Only, for God's sake, lay off the slow-moving stuff. We've had too much of that."

"Slow-moving? Which, for instance?"

"Lines like Cluss & Hein dresses, Shantz coats. You've got several dogs."

Green stiffened. "Those are some of our oldest sources, Mr. Blaze! I'd hate to cut them out!"

"Who said cut them out? If they come up with a good number, fine. But let's not load up with junk that has to be marked down two, even three times before it sells!"

Bernardine said dryly, "What Cluss & Hein needs is a new designer. Ditto goes for Shantz."

Randolph Green sent her a bewildered look. It was as if she had betrayed him. He started to speak, changed his mind.

Paul ignored the by-play. He was back at his desk now, standing behind it, fingering a dozen memos Maud Heller had left. "Okay, Green," he said. "The sooner we start rolling, the better. Try hitting the market tomorrow."

The buyer's face was strained when he walked out. Bernardine looked after him thoughtfully.

"Paul, maybe you touched a sore spot," she said.

"How?"

"Shantz, Cluss & Hein——" She shrugged. "Could be
they're his wife's cousins or something."

"Don't be catty. As far as I'm concerned, they're second-
raters. Hell with them." And then, looking up, Paul said
abruptly, "Berry, what you doing tonight?"

She turned to him in surprise. *"You* tell me."

He rubbed a hand across his stomach. "I'm wound up.
Can we find a quiet place where we can eat in peace?"

"I'm a busy gal and hard to get," Bernardine said. "The
minute we close I'll meet you at the side door."

Immelman's Restaurant, on the road to Medill, occupied
the lower floor of what had once been an enormous private
home. Mama Immelman served authentic Pennsylvania Dutch
food. There was a bowl of sliced cucumbers in vinegar on every
table. There was sauerbraten with a flavor all its own; and apple dumplings, and imported Münchiner beer. The walls were
decorated with hex signs, and the waitresses wore crisp, color-
ful nineteenth-century dresses that flared out over bulging
petticoats.

Mama Immelman's three sons were always there with their
musical instruments—a violin, an accordion, a mandolin.
While they played they walked around the restaurant, and
when they stopped at a table, the guests usually sang with
them. It made Immelman's gay, casual, a delightful place in
which to eat.

Passing among the tables, Bernardine greeted a good many
people she knew. And just before eight o'clock Patrice Selby

came in with a big, lumbering young man Paul recognized—
Warren Graham of the *Reporter*.

If Patrice was at all surprised to find Paul and Bernardine
together, she gave no indication of it. She paused a moment to
talk. Her manner was formal, almost cool. Paul suspected,
with a sense of injustice, that she was holding him responsible
for her father's latest defeat.

Warren Graham told him, "I'll be starting on those institutional ads this week end."

"Fine. Hope you'll find they're fun to do."

Patrice put in, "You couldn't have picked a better writer.
It's a break for the store." And then, "Let's get our table,
Warren."

Her coolness was disturbing. Paul sat down and shook his
head. "What's the matter with these Selbys?" he said. "Can't
they realize I'm in the store to——"

"Uh-uh." Bernardine pressed a finger against his lips.
"You're here to relax."

"All I was going to say——"

"—can wait till later. You took me out for diversion.
And, by heaven, you're going to *be* diverted! No more talk
about the store."

He grinned a bit forcedly and dropped the matter.

How much he needed relief from concentration on Selby's,
he hadn't realized. The music, the food, the noise—it was all a
tonic. By the time he was ready to drive her home, he felt infinitely more at ease. They waved to Patrice and Warren Graham, and left.

"Come up a while," Bernardine said at her door. "I'll give
you apple brandy."

"I was coming even without the brandy."

"Were you? I never know."

Her parents had a home in Gorham, some thirty miles away; so, for convenience, Bernardine maintained this small apartment six blocks from the store. As he glanced around at the Swedish-modern furniture, Paul reflected that her good taste was as evident here as in her clothes.

She poured the apple brandy, and they faced each other from the corners of a long couch. She kicked off her shoes, tucked her feet under her skirt.

"We should do this often," she said. "It's nice."

He smiled as he sipped the brandy. His arm lay on the back of the couch, a cigarette sending up a spiral of smoke from his fingers. And he became thoughtful.

After a long silence Bernardine asked, "What is it, Paul?"

"Just digesting a lesson I learned today. Something I keep telling myself again and again—and always let myself forget." He stared at his glass. "In business you've got to go after what you want—and to hell with whom you hurt. Once you start *worrying* about hurting people, you generally wind up by hurting them all the more."

"A Blaze paradox. And I'm not sure I understand it."

"Forget it."

He sipped his drink, then looked along the length of the couch at Bernardine's burnished hair, at her beautifully made-up face.

"Now," she mocked, "it's finally not the store that's on your mind. It's me."

He nodded.

"What's this problem?" she asked.

"Just trying to make you out."

"Which means that in about ten seconds you'll be giving an imitation of my mother."

"How?"

Chapter
Ten

DONALD RIPLEY, in charge of Selby's displays, was a gaunt, bony man with the melancholy eyes of a spaniel. This evening he sat beside his parlor window. A newspaper lay forgotten in his lap. He gazed at the wall, thinking of the memo he had found on his desk: *Mr. Blaze would like to see you first thing in the morning.*

"Millie," he said in a low voice, "I don't like it."

His wife, a buxom woman who devoted much of her time to volunteer church work, sat at a bridge table, addressing post cards. She answered, "You worry too much."

"My show windows aren't good enough any more," he said. "Not for Paul Blaze."

"They're as good as they always were."

"He made surveys. All week he kept men on the sidewalks, checking off how many people actually stopped to look at the windows. Only 3 per cent, Millie."

She glanced up, adjusting her spectacles, blinking slightly as though she didn't understand.

"Only 3 per cent stopped," he said. "The rest went right by."

"How many are *supposed* to stop?"

Ripley shook his head. It was hard to communicate the growing fear in him. He wasn't even sure he wanted to share it. Yet he had to speak to someone; couldn't keep this thing pent up in himself.

"The men who made this survey—they tell me Blaze says the windows don't—*pull*. They don't *sell*. He wants a—new style. He wants a different kind of display——"

"So what? Give him what he wants."

Ripley swallowed. "The kind of windows he wants, Millie —they're not my style. A girl in a spring dress, running across a field, with blossoms behind her . . ." He shook his head again. "You've got to have a special knack, Millie. It's different. It's an art."

"If it's a window," Millie said, "you can do it."

But Donald Ripley couldn't stop worrying. Deep in his mind he recognized his own limitations. He had started work for the Selby store in the days when you put on a pair of carpet slippers and went into a window and did the best you could with what they gave you. Of course, his ideas had grown with time. He had learned a good deal from studying windows in New York and Philadelphia, from poring over trade magazines, even from watching Halliday's.

But Paul Blaze, he knew, with his New York and Philadelphia experience, was going to insist on a wholly new type of window. Not long ago, at a meeting of merchandise men, he had heard Paul Blaze make the point that about 25 per cent of all sales resulted from impulse buying. And half of these impulses occurred because people saw something attractively displayed.

Suppose, Ripley thought, he found himself unable to meet Mr. Blaze's standards? What then?

He was fifty-seven. What did you do if you were pushed aside at fifty-seven? Who would hire you—especially if you were let out because you couldn't produce displays that "sold"?

He stared at his wife, scribbling her endless post cards. *Millie*, he thought in rising panic, *what if I'm through?* . . .

When Paul entered his office the following morning he found Ben Lork waiting for him. The lean, red-haired controller looked disturbed. He was walking restlessly.

"Paul," he said, "I hear you're seeing Donald Ripley this morning. Like to talk to you about that."

"Sure. Sit down."

"What do you want Ripley to do?"

"Pep up the whole display system, inside and out. Primarily, I want single-figure apparel windows on Main Street, full of action. The Bonwit Teller kind."

Ben Lork shook his head. "It's hopeless, Paul. Not his style."

"In that case," Paul said, "we'll have to find somebody who *can* do them."

"You miss the point. Ripley's been with us twenty-six years. Loyal and hard-working. You can't fire a man like that. My father-in-law would never stand for it. That's one thing he prizes—loyalty to the store. Then there's another consideration —the morale of every co-worker. Ripley's been president of the Co-Workers' Association for six years. He's liked by everybody. You fire a man like that, and all seven hundred co-workers are going to ask: What price loyalty?" Ben paused, then added more quietly, "You'll *need* the support of the co-workers, Paul. You'll never build volume without it. You know that as well as I do."

Paul's fingers toyed with a pencil. Queer, he thought, how the things on which you were most likely to stub your toes were not always the big issues—those you could grapple with. It was too often a thing like this. A relatively small personal matter. A point of sentiment.

Ben was right, of course, when he suggested that a store's first line of contact with the public was its sales force. If they were happy, confident, sure of themselves, they would promote business. If they were scared, insecure, wondering how long their pay envelopes would continue . . . salespeople of that type were no asset.

And yet, could you allow sentiment to shackle the store with dull show windows? Windows that were costing Selby's the loss of thousands a year?

He heard a knock and looked up to see the gaunt, slightly stooped figure of Donald Ripley himself in the door. Melancholy eyes looked down at him questioningly.

"You wanted to see me, Mr. Blaze?"

Paul drew a long breath. "Yes, Ripley. Come in. Have a seat." He said to Ben, "Don't go."

While Ripley sat down, his hands on his knees, Paul leaned back from the desk, crossed his legs.

"Ripley," he said, "Mr. Lork and I have been talking about display. How often, on the average, do we change our windows?"

The unexpected question seemed to catch Ripley off guard. He said, "Why—about every ten days or so."

"And interior displays? At points-of-sale?"

"That depends. Some departments, every couple of weeks —like millinery, for instance. Others, maybe once a month. As I say, it all depends on the department."

"I'd like to speed it all up. Have the store looking fresh, attractive—something new always popping. We ought to have new Main Street windows at least once a week—every three or four days would be even better. Keep people *looking* at them. And I'd like to see point-of-sale displays changed to meet whatever new shipments come in."

Donald Ripley blinked. He stared at Ben, who also seemed surprised. This was hardly what Ripley had come prepared to discuss.

He said, "Well—I don't know, Mr. Blaze—I don't have a big staff. Changes like that—sounds like a lot more work than we could possibly handle unless we add a few more people——"

"That's all right. *Let's* add people." Paul got up, lean and restless, walked to a cooler he'd had installed. As water gurgled into a cup, he said, "Good display is as important as any selling gimmick we could dream up. To a store like this the right kind of display can be worth hundreds of thousands a year. So if we spend a few thousand more to *get* displays that have pull— why, we're making a damned sound investment. High time display got the consideration it deserves at Selby's."

Ripley began, "Mr. Blaze, I've *tried*——"

"Hell, I know. But how can you do a real job with an inadequate staff?"

Ripley swallowed.

Paul said, "If we're going to make the most of display, let's do it in a big way. You're the man to do it, Ripley. Next meeting of the Board, I'm going to ask that you be made

Display Co-ordinator. Supervise everything, windows and points-of-sale. . . . That should be worth a boost in salary, shouldn't it, Ben?"

The controller parted his lips. He sought words, but they didn't come. After a moment he said limply, "I—I should think so, yes."

"Now, Ripley," Paul said, his manner brisk, "what I'd like you to do is get to New York as damn fast as you can. Find the best assistants you can put your hands on—men with up-to-the-minute ideas—one who's experienced in single-figure window displays and one for the inside point-of-sale job. We'll pay whatever we have to. Get the best you can dig up. I'd give a lot to land somebody who's been doing the Bonwit Teller or Saks Fifth Avenue jobs. . . . Think you could leave today?"

"Why——" Ripley was stunned. "Why, I——"

"It'll be an operation that may yield as much as a half-million a year. So find a window man who's popping with ideas. Same goes for the inside man. This whole deal will be your responsibility, Ripley. Okay?"

There was silence. Stiffly, then, like a man in a daze, Donald Ripley pushed himself up from the chair. He was pale. The muscles in his face were working in a strange way. He glanced again at Ben Lork, whose eyes were averted, and back at Paul.

In a low, unsteady voice he said, "I—I guess I can catch the afternoon train. Sure. I'll get busy on it right away, Mr. Blaze. Thanks."

When he started for the door, Paul sat down, feeling embarrassed. It always embarrassed him to see signs of tears in a man. He began to fuss with papers on the desk.

Suddenly Ripley turned. He had already reached the door,

her self-respect, Martha had to answer with emphatic conviction that she did love him. The only way to justify what she had been doing for the past year was to believe she loved Jerry. Certainly he made her *feel* she was in love.

Nevertheless that taunting inner voice persisted with its jibes, asking again and again: *Could* a woman of fifty truly fall in love with a man of thirty-nine? . . .

She answered by falling back on arguments about the powers of the involuntary. There were a thousand human reactions over which the human being had no control: Could you avoid perspiring in excessive heat? Could you avoid shivering in the cold? Could you dictate the rate of your heart-beat? A woman was subject to involuntary reactions in every aspect of her life, including its emotional aspects. Martha was not responsible, really, for these natural feelings toward Jerry Weed. . . . Or so she tried to tell herself.

It was almost a year since she had first met him. She had come to a convention of women's organizations in New York, and Jerry had addressed one of the luncheons. She still remembered his big, handsome figure as she had seen it that first time —the humor in his black eyes, in the things he said as he spoke to the delegates. His first play, *My Secretary,* was running through its five-week span on Broadway at the time. The author of such a play was the perfect guest for a women's convention. Martha had thoroughly enjoyed his speech.

As program chairman she sat beside him at the luncheon table. After his talk she had a great deal of merry conversation with Jerry. And when she admitted, somewhat ruefully, that she had not yet seen *My Secretary,* he jotted her hotel address into his memorandum book.

Within a few hours, at her hotel, Martha had been surprised by a telephone call.

"How would you like to see *My Secretary* tomorrow night?" he had asked.

"Why, I'd love it, Mr. Weed!"

"Suppose I pick you up for dinner at six-thirty. . . ."

That was how it had started; it had gone on for almost a year now. She liked to think that Jerry wasn't really so much younger than she. Jerry, in truth, was ageless. When he took her into his arms, it was his manhood, not his years, that mattered.

And yet, in moments of clearheaded speculation, Martha knew their association was in some ways a delusion. She was no fool. She understood herself all too well, and what she saw was not flattering.

She had come to a time of life when everything in her, physically and mentally, seemed insecure, shaken, changing. She was losing her hold even on her middle years, and that was a shocking thing to realize. Jerry represented rescue and reassurance. When she was with him she felt young, vital, important to him and to herself.

And whom was this affair harming? No one. Some people might disapprove, of course. She was well aware that Everett, for instance, might be shocked. But it did Everett no real harm.

Even the money she occasionally spent on gifts for Jerry took nothing away from Everett. He had his own income, his own successful job. He needed no financial help from her.

In this facet of her life, Martha felt, she need consider nobody but herself. For her Jerry Weed was good. He made her come alive. . . .

When she reached his apartment his delight in seeing her was exactly the tonic she needed. He held her arms, standing back so that he might admire her whole figure.

"Martha, you look beautiful!"

He was big, six-feet-two and well over two hundred pounds in weight. He had a vigorous, well-formed figure and dark hair incapable of staying combed.

His right arm gave her another hug, playful this time, as he drew her to a chair. "Sit down while I fix a drink," he said. "Then we'll go over to Ferrari's for dinner. . . ."

That evening, talking with Jerry about his new play, she told herself again that loving him couldn't be wrong. She was in desperate need of this sense of exaltation.

She had never had any serious thoughts about actually marrying him. He had never spoken of it, and neither had she. True, she was occasionally jealous—for brief, poignant seconds which she managed somehow to crush; jealous of those women he must know, go out with, while she remained in Williston. He didn't talk of them, nor did she ask questions. That way lay masochism. Why invite pain?

It was enough that she had him when she was here. She could be happy to let this relationship go on eternally, and she knew of only one way of insuring that: by doing whatever she could for Jerry.

He had finished his third act, he said. "But where do we go from here?" He sounded discouraged. "That's the big question."

"Has Crossley read it?"

Ralph Crossley had produced his first play. It was natural for Jerry to turn to him with this one.

"He likes it, all right," he said. "But what good is it when he can't find angels?"

"How about Crossley himself?"

"You know Ralph. He's never yet put a cent into a play."

"Jerry." Martha caught his hand in reassurance. "Don't worry. We'll raise the money."

He sighed. Martha could understand how he felt. It was a long time since she had promised she would help find the eighty thousand dollars required for the play. She bent toward him.

"Darling, you've got to have patience. Things are really moving now. The store is bound to have the biggest summer in its history. As its volume goes up, the value of my stock will go up. Right now I can't borrow all of eighty thousand dollars on it, but give me a few months more——"

A brief laugh fell from Jerry. "Who'd believe it?" he said. "A play depending on the amount of business done by a department store."

"Jerry, I give you my word——"

She was so earnest that he turned to look at her. Maybe he realized how much she needed him, for he suddenly took her into his arms.

Martha closed her eyes with a kind of pain. Her hands clutched at him. She hung onto Jerry. Only Jerry could make her feel like this—young, alive, glowing. You lived for moments of happiness like these. If you found them, all else was worth the doing. . . .

Chapter
Twelve

IN THE FIRST WEEK OF MAY the effects of the new policy at the Selby store began to assert themselves. Every morning huge black streamers reading *Today at Selby's* ran across double-page newspaper spreads, announcing slashes on special items. By Friday, after five days of it, Everett Selby jubilantly declared that the ads were hitting the town like H-bombs.

Late that morning Grace Lork dropped in at her sister's. She found Patrice at work in her studio. Grace sat on the huge square hassock that sometimes served as a pedestal for models. Eyes slightly narrowed, she watched the final deft touches put on the picture of a young bride.

In paint-smeared dungarees and a yellow pullover sweater, Patrice looked small and slight—so compellingly attractive that for an annoyed instant Grace rebelled again, as she had a thousand times, at the fact that this blond sister of hers paid so little attention to the men who were interested in her. It was absurd to allow that wretched affair in France to block other men.

Warren Graham, for example. Warren was intelligent, able, personable. The editorials he wrote for the *Reporter* were making him something of a public figure. True, he had never earned much money by Selby standards. But this could hardly have troubled Patrice. Besides, now that Warren was writing the store's half-page institutional advertisements, he was earning considerably more.

How long these writings would continue, Grace could not know. Several of them had already appeared, and they were excellent, she thought. Her friends had made a point of telling her how revealing they were.

Grace said, "I've just come from the store. Pat, it's amazing."

Patrice continued painting. "Is it? Haven't been there in several days."

"I don't know when I've seen so many people in the place."

Patrice's reply was dry. "People always rush to a cut-rate store."

"Oh, be yourself. Give the man credit.'

Patrice stepped back from the easel to squint at what she had done. The bridal figure had the hazy quality characteristic of everything she painted.

"That's very good," Grace said.

Patrice accepted the compliment in silence. She turned, wiping her hands on a bit of cloth. "So the store is crowded," she said. "But when all the ballyhoo is over, when all accounts are settled, I wonder if Selby's will earn more than it did last year."

"Of course it will!"

"When you consider what Paul is spending on promotion, and the fact that he's selling at slashed prices, all this increased volume may be just a lot of hoop-la. The test is: how much is left at the end of the year?"

Grace rose. "*I'm* perfectly willing to suspend judgment till we see. I've noticed, though, that even Ben has become more optimistic—and Ben, who spends every minute of his day with the figures, doesn't cheer up easily. You know Ben." She looked at her wrist watch. "I've got to run."

Patrice answered, "You see *Ben*. You don't see Dad every night. I do. I don't like what's happening to him."

"I don't like it, either," Grace agreed. "On the other hand, it seems silly to make a tragedy of this. If Paul Blaze succeeds, doesn't Dad stand to benefit as much as anyone else? If Paul fails——" She shrugged. "He'll be out, and Dad'll be running the show his way again. I don't see why we have to treat this like a national disaster. . . . Anyhow, go see the store if you get a chance. . . ."

Patrice could not resist the urging. She drove to Selby's that afternoon.

There were two special sales—one in women's dresses, the other in housewares. And she stared in astonishment at the size of the crowds they had attracted.

In order to see what was happening on every floor, she went all the way to the sixth by escalator. Coming down, she stopped in the dress department. This had advertised one of the specials. It seemed to her that hundreds of women were milling around the racks.

And suddenly, while she watched, the public address system caught her attention. The voice of George Weaver, the store's announcer, delivered the kind of message she had never before heard in Selby's. She listened in bewilderment.

"Your attention, please! It is now four o'clock. This is a bonus announcement for everyone who will be in Selby's half an hour from now. Exactly at 4:30 the umbrella department on the third floor will begin a sensational sale. It will last for one hour only, until closing. During that hour every umbrella in stock will be sold at 20 per cent below its marked price. . . . Don't miss this opportunity! For one hour only! If you can use an umbrella, if you know anyone who would appreciate an umbrella as a gift, this is your chance to save 20 per cent . . . 4:30 at the umbrella department on the third floor! Thank you!"

Puzzled, Patrice went to the umbrella department where Henry Kogler, the fat little manager, was instructing the extra help which had been sent by personnel.

"What's all this ballyhoo?" she asked.

Kogler grinned. "A different department every day, Miss Selby. One-hour sales, unadvertised. A break for people who happen to be in the store."

She must have looked dubious, because Kogler added:

"Yesterday, for one hour, they ran a 20 per cent slash on handbags. They did over $600!"

She turned away, frowning. No doubt Paul knew how to produce business. He had ideas by the score. Yet she found herself recoiling from this use of the public address system. It filled Selby's with announcements like a circus barker's. . . .

And wasn't it, she wondered, the wrong kind of day to ask people to think about umbrellas? There was a bright spring sun outside; the afternoon was warm. Nevertheless, in the next half-hour, she heard the announcement repeated three times.

Just before 4:30, driven by curiosity, Patrice went to watch results. More than forty people were already crowded at the umbrella counters. Others were arriving.

After the sale began she tried to count the umbrella transactions as co-workers wrote their slips. In fifteen minutes she tallied 18. That *could* mean over 70 in the allotted hour.

Driving homeward, she was troubled by conflicting reactions. "Give the man credit," Grace had said, and no doubt

Grace was right. If your only concern was increasing business, Paul Blaze was doing a good job. Why, then, have misgivings? Yet she kept worrying about her father. . . .

And she remembered, for no clear reason, the time she had met Paul at Immelman's Restaurant with Bernardine Sorel. It was not the only time she had encountered him with Bernardine. Only a few evenings ago, driving past the Williston Hotel shortly after nine, she had seen them come out together. She wondered, with a vague frown, if Paul Blaze was developing Williston interests beyond those of promoting sales.

Bernardine was attractive. Very. Patrice couldn't blame the man. Besides, she thought with abrupt harshness, what business was it of *hers?*

She stepped on the accelerator with an unreasonable sense of anger, raced up the winding hill of Warwick Road.

That afternoon Paul received a letter from a firm which proposed installing radio-telephones in the Selby delivery trucks. "The advantages, as proved by a number of department stores throughout the nation, are considerable," the letter insisted. "For example, in the matter of pick-ups of merchandise to be returned to the store. Instead of making a special trip to an address, the delivery truck in that area is notified by telephone, and it makes the pick-up in passing. Mistakes in loading, too, can quickly be checked. If a package has been loaded on the wrong truck, a telephone call can locate the error in a few seconds. . . ."

This, he decided, was something to be turned over to Conrad Selby for study by the delivery department. So he crossed the corridor, but at Selby's door he paused.

The gray-haired president stood in conversation with an elderly woman. A Persian lamb coat lay spread on Selby's desk.

"How long ago did you buy this from us?" he was asking.

"Twelve years, I think. Maybe thirteen. The point is it's no longer good enough to wear. Yet I feel it's too good to be thrown away. What do you think I ought to do with it, Mr. Selby?"

Running a hand over the fur, Selby answered, "Frankly, Mrs. Wright, I would not advise you to have it remodeled. It would need too many additional skins to make it worth doing."

"I'd hate to discard it——"

"No need. Why not let us use it for the lining of a cloth coat? We could make up a beauty—either for you or your daughter. You'd get years out of it that way. You wouldn't have to buy any additional skins at all."

Paul went back to his own desk. Obviously there was one thing Conrad Selby had won for himself—the respect and confidence of customers. Mrs. Wright was not the first whom Paul had seen come to the president for advice. By and large, they were the old-timers whose families had patronized Selby's for generations. They liked to maintain a personal relationship with the owners of the store. It flattered them, Paul suspected, to have the president himself take an interest in their shopping problems. And Conrad Selby did this well, with dignity, with friendliness, with honesty of purpose.

Paul was a good enough merchandiser to know that such a relationship was invaluable. He had, in fact, urged all Selby co-workers to stimulate friendly personal relationships with customers. "It's as important to please them as to sell them," he had said. "If you please them, they'll come back for many more purchases." Conrad Selby himself had long ago made an art of this.

Now the president looked into his door. "Did you want to see me, Paul?"

"Oh . . . yes." Paul came around the desk to hand Selby the letter concerning radio-telephones. "Thought you might want to give this some consideration."

"Thanks." Selby's voice was dry. He glanced at the letter, thrust it into a side pocket. "By the way, about the spot sales announced over the public address system——"

"They did pretty well," Paul said with a grin.

"Reminded me of the fair grounds. With barkers yelling, 'Step this way! Biggest bargain in town!' "

"It's not that bad," Paul said. "Besides, this last one sold about eighty umbrellas—for a gross of almost $600."

Selby gave Paul a long, thoughtful stare. Then he turned away, expressionless. But Paul quickly stopped him.

"You don't approve?"

"I don't like the method."

"If I'm making a mistake, I'd like to know where."

Again Selby looked at him in that appraising way. Then he came back and lowered himself into one of the leather chairs. He rested his elbows on its arms and clasped his fingers in an arc.

"Paul, I can't honestly say you're making a mistake. It may well be that you're right and I'm wrong. Certainly the weight of evidence is entirely on your side, measured in dollars and cents. What it gets down to is a difference in points of view. I see no reason why you should accept mine, however— any more than I can wholly accept yours."

"That still doesn't tell me what's wrong with those spot sales."

"Nothing is wrong with them—as long as your sole objective is increasing volume. You're primarily interested in *how much* we make. I'm interested in that, too, of course—but I'm also concerned with *how* we make it. . . . You see, I feel the store's reputation and mine are indivisible. And there are certain kinds of dollars I'd rather not have."

"There are certain kinds of dollars I'd rather not have myself," Paul said. He could not hide his rising resentment. Why should Selby imply that there was something unethical in his methods? He said, "I wouldn't want dollars earned out of dope, for instance. I wouldn't want dollars earned out of gypping customers. But we're giving them honest merchandise—and one hundred cents' worth for every dollar they spend!"

"I know."

"What's objectionable in that?"

Conrad Selby considered the question in silence. Finally he said, "Suppose, Paul, someone suggested that we hire sandwich men to parade up and down Main Street. Carrying big 'Shop at Selby's' placards. Would you do it?"

"I doubt it."

"Why?"

"That kind of advertising wouldn't be at all representative of the store."

"You mean it would lack dignity. Exactly." Selby rose now. "Our differences, Paul, are after all only a matter of degree. We both have our individual concepts of what makes for dignity in selling, of what constitutes a store's character and integrity. . . . I'm afraid that's the only way I can explain it. Call it a difference in taste."

"Personally," Paul said, "I see nothing whatever undignified in the spot sales."

"Then there's really no point in talking further, is there?" Selby gave him a vague smile and a nod. "Well, I'll see you in the morning. Good night."

When Selby had gone, Paul sat at the desk, his fingers pattering nervously on the blotting pad. He knew what was wrong. Only, it was the kind of thing he couldn't say to Conrad Selby. The difference between them was this: Selby had known the comfort of money all his life. He had never been forced to fight for it. Now it shocked him to see somebody else go all-out, by every available method, to make money. Whereas Paul himself, *wanting* the kind of money Selby already had, knew he had to fight and struggle for it.

Damn it, he thought, *I've got to pick the way that pays off!*

Chapter

Thirteen

Brian Halliday, the short, stocky president of the Halliday store, stood behind his desk. The morning *Reporter* lay unfolded before him. He studied the Selby advertisements through the smoke of the cigar his fingers kept rolling between his lips.

The page on the left featured women's summer suits. Some extremely smart garments were illustrated. Huge letters announced that for one day only these specials would be sold at the drastically reduced prices of $29.95 and $19.95. The opposite page advertised a one-day sale on rugs and broadloom carpeting.

Halliday took the cigar from his mouth. He looked around the office at his two sons, Roger and Craig, and at Charlie Clay, his head merchandise manager.

"No way to find out?" he asked.

Nobody answered.

Brian Halliday grunted. So far no one had discovered a way of learning in advance what items Selby's planned to put on sale from day to day. If there were a means of discovering this, Halliday's could match the sales; Halliday's could offer timely competition. But you had to have advance information in order to prepare the right merchandise and price tickets in time, in order to run competing advertisements.

"All you see in this goddam sheet is Selby's, Selby's, Selby's!" he said.

It was costing him more than he liked to admit. During the past two weeks, in whatever department Selby's had offered a daily special, the comparable department at Halliday's had suffered a sharp decline. Today, for example, with Selby's advertising women's summer suits at 20 per cent to 50 per cent below their normal prices, how many summer suits could Halliday's hope to sell? And Selby's was asking $4.44 a yard for the same broadloom carpeting for which, this morning, Halliday's was charging $5.26.

He said to Charlie Clay, "Thought you were friendly with practically everybody at Selby's."

"Sure," Clay answered. "But not so friendly they tell me ahead of time what Selby's is going to do."

"What about the boys at the newspaper?"

"I tried. The only time they find out what's cooking is when the copy comes in. Too late for us."

"Well, damn it, *somebody* must be in on the planning of these sales! Somebody besides Blaze and Selby!"

"Sure. There's Ben Lork and Everett Selby. You expect *them* to spout?"

"There must be others. Layout people. Buyers. Stenographers. Anybody!"

Charlie Clay, whose parched skin was almost as gray as his hair, shrugged wearily. "Why should they talk? Do we tell Selby's what *we're* going to do?"

Brian Halliday's two sons began to argue that their store's best course was to concentrate on its own sales, ignoring what

Selby's did. But Halliday seemed not to hear this. He was frowning at the two-page spread of specials.

"There must be *some* way to find out," he repeated. He glanced at his two sons. They both frowned at the floor. "What the hell, Roger, you see enough of that fashion dame—what's her name?"

"Look, Pop," Roger replied. "Bernardine Sorel won't talk about things like that."

"What the hell *do* you two talk about?"

Roger, who took Bernardine out every week or two, grinned. "Not about business," he said. "You think I'm a dope? . . ."

The Selby store's new type of show windows were unveiled on the morning of May 14th, a day before the regular monthly meeting of the Board of Directors.

Walking from his hotel, Paul saw that they were drawing attention even at 9:15. He smiled. When displays could stop people hurrying to work, they were effective. Of course, there was the novelty factor to be considered in this first group of new presentations; but whatever the reason, there were people at almost every window.

It seemed to him, as he passed, that the displays were as attractive as any he had ever seen in New York, with only one mannequin in each window. The figures were gracefully posed against seasonal backgrounds. Donald Ripley, he thought with gratification, had found a couple of able assistants in Harold Quincey Coombs and Alfred Horn.

From his desk he telephoned Ripley as soon as he sat down.

"They're elegant windows, Donald," he said. "Congratulations!"

The man sounded pleased and excited. "We're working on the new point-of-sale settings now," he said. "Wait'll you see what we come up with *there!* We'll have some ready tomorrow!"

"Good."

As he put the telephone down Paul glanced up to see Bernardine enter, looking her best in a bottle-green suit. She carried a dress and a summer wrap into the office.

He asked, "Like the windows?"

"They're fine." But obviously her mind was on something else. "Paul, what do you think of these?"

She held up the dress first—a white polka-dotted number, half-sleeved, with a conventional neckline. She spread the summer wrap over a chair. It seemed to Paul that both garments were without particular distinction; run-of-the-mill merchandise. Nothing to feature in a store that prided itself on its fashions.

"The dress is marked $35," Bernardine said. "The wrap sells for $59.95."

Paul whistled.

"Point is," she added, "we're getting big shipments of both these numbers. What are we going to *do* with them?"

Paul asked, "Whose lines?"

"The dress is Cluss & Hein. The wrap is Shantz."

He rose, surprised. "Thought I'd asked Green to lay off their junk!"

"You did."

"So what's the idea? Where is he?"

"New York. Due back for tomorrow's Board meeting."

"How much of this is he sending in?"

"The Cluss & Hein order runs to $900. The Shantz to about $400."

Paul said with irritation, "Get him on the phone, Berry. Tell him to cancel. I *told* him not to load us up with dead wood!"

Bernardine asked, "Orders from the boss? To cancel?"

"Absolutely!"

She gathered up the dress and the wrap and left.

Paul was annoyed. There were things about Randolph Green he couldn't understand. The man was able—no doubt about that. And he knew the market. He was finding special buys that were magnificent. He was shipping in some of the best merchandise the store had to offer. And in the midst of his good work he loaded up with stuff like this. . . . What had got *into* the man?

Bernardine's telephone call stopped Randolph Green in New York just as he was about to leave his hotel room. When he finished talking, he sat stunned. He took off his hat, put it on the bed. He drew the handkerchief from his breast pocket, daubing it around the edge of his collar. Orders from Blaze, she had said. Green felt as if Paul Blaze had slapped him across the mouth.

He stared at the telephone, hesitating to touch it again, yet knowing he must. In the end he drew in his lips and called Cluss & Hein.

"If you're worrying about the dresses," Morris Hein said

cheerfully, "you can relax, Ranny. They're on the racks right now, ready to be packed and shipped."

Green swallowed. "Morris—hold them. I—I've got to cancel."

This time there was no reply.

Green said, "Sorry, Morris. Orders from home."

Then Morris Hein, as though he had just found his breath, blurted, "For God's sake, Ranny, what do you mean—cancel? You can't do a thing like this to me! They're *ready!* All made up——"

"Morris, I'm on a spot——"

"*You're* on a spot! Where do you think *I* am? Nine hundred dollars' worth of goods!"

"I'll make up for it, Morris. You'll have other numbers."

"What am I supposed to do with this lot? Give 'em to the Red Cross?"

"Take it easy, boy. It's good merchandise. Somebody'll pick it up."

"Sure! Some damned bargain hunter!" And Morris Hein said with a groan, "Nine hundred bucks! Dead on the racks! What are you *doing* to me?"

"Morris, you've got to play along. I've never had to do a thing like this before."

"In your case even *once* is too often! When I think how much we've advanced——"

"All right, all right."

Green managed somehow to end the ordeal. He still had to speak to Herbert Shantz, and his forehead was wet. He gulped down a pill, then looked around the room with harried eyes. If at that instant he could have thought of some way to hit back at Paul Blaze, he'd have done it with consummate satisfaction. . . .

Though he went through the trial of canceling the Shantz order, he was not yet finished with the day's demands. He walked about the hotel room, nervous, rubbing the palms of his hands together. Finally he went back to the telephone. This time he called a Butterfield exchange number.

"Hello, Cherry," he said.

A girl's voice, suppressing a long yawn, answered, "Yes, Ranny. . . . Good God, what time is it? I'm still in bed——"

"Sorry. Look, kid. About tonight. We'd better call it off. I've got to go back——"

"*Ranny!*" Abruptly she sounded wide-awake. Her tones became suspicious, then harsh. "What are you trying to do? Give me a run-around?"

"Look, Cherry——"

"Breaking three dates in a row! . . . Listen, pal, if you *want* to call it quits——"

"I can't help it, Cherry. I—I've run into trouble."

She was sarcastic now. "What's her name?"

"It's not that, Cherry. It's business—a bad business break——"

"Boloney!"

"Cherry, listen——"

"Why don't you come clean? You've been cooling off on me for weeks. You know that. You want out?"

Green could not answer. The truth was it no longer mattered. With so many other things on his mind, it was hard to be concerned about Cherry. He looked at the floor.

She launched a harangue. It was bitter and taunting in the beginning, but after a time its tenor changed to studied indifference. If he was tired of the situation, she said, there was nothing to hold him. Not a thing. Nor her, either. She'd get along fine. In fact, without him she might even get along better.

In the end, when she angrily hung up, Green wiped the perspiration from his face. He knew he should be feeling beaten, but instead he had an astonishing sense of release. He picked up his hat and started for the door. Now that it was done, he wanted as quickly as possible to get into the market. . . .

Chapter
Fourteen

A FEW MINUTES before the regular monthly Board of Directors' meeting on the 15th, Paul had a long-distance call from Martin Traub, the men's-wear buyer, who was in New York. If you judged by the excitement in Traub's voice, he had struck a bonanza.

"Mr. Blaze," he said, "could you possibly come to New York? To Weller & Dunn?" Weller & Dunn were men's retail clothiers. Traub said, "They're closing out. Building's coming down. They'll sell out their whole inventory—one big lot—to the highest bidder."

Paul asked, "How many bidding?"

"At least a dozen, including two department stores. We could clean up on this! I think you could buy this inventory for maybe 30 cents on the dollar."

"How many suits?"

"Close to 1,600. Also 600 coats. Hell of a big deal."

Paul's pencil did some rapid arithmetic. At the wholesale level approximately $90,000 worth of merchandise could be bought for $30,000 or less, if Traub was right. He recalled that a New York department store, taking advantage of a similar opportunity a few years ago, had disposed of more than 3,000

suits in a single three-day sale. That wouldn't happen in Williston, but he might get another store to share the buy. . . .

"Put in a bid," he said.

"They want to deal only with top management."

"Okay. I'll catch the evening train. Meet you at Weller &
Dunn's at 9:30 tomorrow."

When he had put the telephone down, Paul asked Maud
Heller to reserve a hotel room in New York.

"The Barkley all right?" Maud said. "We've got an account there. It's where the Selbys always go."

Paul nodded as he went off to the meeting in the conference room.

There was an unusual sense of expectation at this Board
meeting. Because it was a month since the first promotional
policies of the new general manager had been announced, there
would no doubt be an accounting of what the month had produced.

Conrad Selby, calm and grave, sat at the head of the table. The twelve directors lined its sides, and Paul, at the far
end, occupied a chair directly opposite Selby's, his back to
Patrice's painting of the store.

Paul was puzzled by a new attitude in the president. In
the past two days, since Selby had made a trip to the National
Retail Dry Goods Association in New York, his manner had
been more conciliatory. Though Paul was gratified by the
change, he could not understand it. What, he wondered, had
happened in New York?

"Before we formally start the meeting I want to compliment our general manager," Selby began, "on several of our recent innovations. The new windows, for example—I'm sure all of us are quite happy about them."

It was odd that at a moment like this, with Selby so cordial, a warning should slip from a remote recess of Paul's memory. Six weeks ago, he recalled, Everett had said to him, *A great guy, my uncle. Quiet, dignified, restrained. But when he's quietest—look out. That's when he's apt to cut loose with a haymaker. . . .*

"I'm also pleased," Selby went on, "by the effects of the incentive bonuses we announced a few weeks ago. You've probably noticed, as I have, the new enthusiasm, the new eagerness of every co-worker. Mr. Blaze was right in that—there's no better way to increase sales than by giving everybody a personal stake in creating more business. Lately I have watched co-workers induce customers to look at items which, a few weeks ago, would have been ignored. I'm sure Ben will tell you, when he makes his report, that there has been a marked increase in multiple sales."

Selby paused to light a cigar. When he had tossed the match aside, he continued:

"Frankly, however, I do *not* like the unadvertised specials announced over the public address system. I've already expressed my opinion to Mr. Blaze. To me this is a kind of circus barker technique. On the other hand, I realize these sales *have* run between $400 and $800 a day. They *could* amount to about $120,000 a year."

He glanced down at the agenda before him.

"Also, I see that under New Business there will be a motion to promote Donald Ripley to a new position—Display Coordinator—with an appropriate increase in salary. I should say this is a reward Ripley richly deserves."

Paul saw that virtually everyone at the table nodded approbation. There would be no question about Ripley's promotion.

"With these preliminary observations out of the way," Selby said, "we can call the meeting to order."

Everett raised his hand.

"Is it all right at this point to say a word about Warren Graham's institutional half-pages?" he asked. "So far eight of them have appeared. They've brought more than a hundred letters. One from the dean of the School of Business Administration at Borden College."

Selby said, "That's very gratifying."

Paul continued to watch the store's president with uncertainty. Whatever it was that had changed his attitude, he kept it well concealed behind his impassivity. . . .

The highlight of this meeting was, as everyone had anticipated, the controller's report. Ben Lork read it from page after page of statistics. It indicated that even those departments which had not yet had daily specials were gaining volume because of the increase of traffic through the store.

"On a store-wide basis," Ben concluded, "during the past month our total business has risen 60 per cent above the volume we showed for the same month last year."

Mark Reickert slapped the table. "*Now* we're getting somewhere!" His face beamed. "Up 60 per cent! This is the best report the Board's heard in years!"

Martha put in, "It's the best report I've *ever* heard!"

Paul glanced at Conrad Selby. He was impassive. . . .

After that, with a 60 per cent increase to dazzle the directors, minor matters were disposed of quickly and without debate. The session might have rolled on to swift adjournment, except for the point Randolph Green unexpectedly raised.

Green, who had arrived from New York some fifteen minutes before the meeting, looked nettled as he lifted his hand. "A question I'd like to ask, Mr. Selby. Concerns my department."

"Yes?"

"Just before I left New York I ran into Si Berman of Claire Duroche." Claire Duroche was one of the leading French *couturières,* with branch offices and showrooms in New York. "Si told me our store—Mr. Blaze himself, in fact—had been dickering with Claire Duroche for an exclusive Paris original. A dress that would have to carry a retail ticket of at least $900. . . . This was news to me. Is it a fact?"

Paul felt mildly exasperated. He wished Randolph Green hadn't yet brought this to the Board's attention. The time was hardly ripe for a discussion of plans still in an early formative stage.

Glancing around the table, he saw startled expressions. Conrad Selby, too, had raised his brows. These people weren't ready for a $900 dress. In fact, the head of the service department, white-haired Walter Bliss, asked in amazement, "Who's going to buy a thing like that?"

"I don't expect anybody to buy it," Paul answered. "I want it for its advertising value. When word gets around that a $900 dress is on display at Selby's, every woman in town is going to want to have a look. With that dress we can generate $10,000 worth of advertising pull."

Walter Bliss, still bewildered, pressed, "You mean we'd invest in a $900 dress without any expectation of selling it?"

"Merely for the purpose of staging a—a side show?" Selby asked.

"Not a side show. A drawing card."

"In Williston," Randolph Green declared, "a dress like

that could drive hundreds of people *away* from the store!"

"How's that?"

"A lot of our customers are the wives of miners, of factory workers. Once they identify Selby's with clothes that are priced way out of reach, they're apt to feel this isn't the store for them."

Paul could not agree. "That's like saying Macy's would lose business if it showed a $40,000 cabin cruiser. No. I'm convinced the dress *would* draw. And apart from its attraction as a curiosity, it would have another purpose."

Randolph Green tried to interrupt again, but Paul drove on:

"Any store that carries Paris originals at $900 is bound to get the reputation of being highly fashion-conscious. A woman out to buy clothes—even if it's only a $16.95 dress—wants to buy it in a store that *is* fashion-conscious. The display of top-flight originals like this Claire Duroche—and I'm contemplating a whole string of them—will more than pay for itself."

He glanced at Bernardine, knowing that what he was about to add would surprise her.

"In line with this general fashion policy," he continued, "I want our Fashion Co-ordinator to go to Paris at least once a year." He saw Bernardine start, her eyes widening. "We'll *publicize* Bernardine's trips. Get them into the papers when she leaves and when she comes back. After trips like that, she'll pull twice as many women to her fashion shows."

Conrad Selby, taking off his glasses, said, "I don't object to Bernardine's going to Paris. In fact, I approve. But as to this matter of investing in $900 gowns which we know we're never going to sell——" He shook a dubious head. "This strikes me as pure theatricalism."

Green said abruptly, "Waste of money!"

With the exception of Bernardine, who argued for the plan, most of the others appeared reluctant to endorse the idea. Paul decided not to make an issue of it. "Let's drop it!" he said. But he was disturbed. Had he misjudged his strength? Did this disapproval mean that, in spite of the spectacular business increase of the past month, the Board was not yet willing wholly to accept his leadership?

Ten minutes after the meeting ended Bernardine came into his office. She shut the door behind her, leaned back against it. "Feel whipped?"

"Just shoved back a little."

"Forget it. That setback didn't mean a thing. Not as an indication of the Board's real feelings."

He sent her an oblique glance. "How do you figure that?"

"It's one thing to vote against Conrad Selby in a closed ballot on a major policy matter. It's another to shove your defiance into his face over a dress. He's still president. Nine members of the Board still work for him. There's a limit to how far they want to risk their standing."

"*You* risked it."

"I'm different. The reckless type." She smiled. "Thanks for the trip to Paris."

Paul tapped a cigarette on the desk. "Showing Paris originals is a damned good idea. Can't understand Green's not seeing it that way. His department."

"He was just sore."

"About the cancellations?"

"Not only that. You went over his head on this Claire Duroche deal."

"Strictly a matter of promotion. Not a buyer's problem. Why put his time on it?"

Bernardine studied the tense, hard lines of his face. "What you need," she decided, "is a chance to recover from a setback. Let's go somewhere tonight."

"Can't. I'll be in New York."

"Oh? Too bad." She was disappointed, but after a pause she brightened. "By the way, didn't you get the impression that Selby is sort of—thawing out? Beginning to accept the situation with better grace? That should make you feel easier."

Paul didn't reply. All his intuitions warned him to be on guard against this change in Selby.

He looked at his watch, rose, buttoned his jacket. He'd have to leave early today to pack a bag. . . .

All the way to New York he wondered about Selby's attitude, but he could find no answer in the events of the past few days. At 9:30 that evening he checked in at the Barkley Hotel in New York. He followed a bellhop toward the elevator. And as he passed the magazine stand he stopped. He stared into the startled eyes of Patrice.

"*Well!*" he said. His feelings were suddenly mixed—part pleasure, part discomfort, part confusion.

Chapter
Fifteen

SHE WAS WEARING a navy-blue suit with a couple of red flowers pinned below the shoulder. Her short blond hair, freshly set and waved, seemed to shine with a glow of its own. She had often irritated Paul, but she certainly didn't look irritating tonight.

The bellhop, holding a bag, waited patiently while they talked. Minutes passed. The girl clasped a magazine under her arm; the lean man smiled down at her.

At last Paul glanced at the hotel clock. "How about giving me a few seconds to wash up? Then we might have a drink."

"If you like."

When he came down he took her to the Club Caracas. In the cab, where he was acutely aware of the gardenia perfume she used, she told him she was in New York on one of her regular visits to see art editors. She had come on the afternoon train.

He watched her face in the darkness. It was small and sensitive and, he thought, extremely pretty when she allowed herself to relax. . . .

At the Club Caracas the captain greeted Paul as an old

friend. He led them to a little round table a few feet from the piano and Marita Gray.

Marita—a striking redhead in a long sheath of flashing metallic cloth—stood in front of a microphone, doing her torch songs in a husky voice. A spotlight was trained on her face. At the moment the rest of the Club Caracas was dark.

In some ways, Paul felt, it was fortunate that they had arrived during Marita's half-hour of entertainment. They could listen without talking. He wasn't sure what he *could* talk about with Patrice. He felt uneasy.

When Marita's performance was over and the dim lights came on again, Patrice gave him a pleasant smile. Their table was hardly twelve inches in diameter. You had to sit very close together in the Club Caracas. Paul glanced over her hair and back to her eyes.

"You look very well," he said.

"Getting away from home," she answered, "always makes me feel—different. It's like throwing off a cloak. I guess geography does something to the spirit."

"Could be that highball."

She laughed. It occurred to him it was the first time he had seen Patrice actually laugh. And he liked it.

"If it's the highball," she said, "get me another, please."

There was a small, smooth orchestra. The dance floor, too, was small. Several couples were rising.

Paul nodded toward the music. "Shall we give it a try?"

"Why not?"

He had only skepticism for his own dancing ability. But there was something about dancing with Patrice that surprised him. He was unexpectedly good at it. Very good. Whatever he did, she became part of the movement. She felt small and slight and airy in his arms, and her body flowed smoothly, almost instinctively, with his own. Everything he did seemed miraculously right.

Her blond head came to his chin. He could smell the gardenia perfume again. And when he glanced down he saw that she, too, was apparently enjoying this.

They danced a good deal. Once, while they rested between numbers, Patrice said: "About this magic of getting away from home—you, too, seem different here."

"Better?"

"Definitely."

He grinned. "Brings up an interesting question. What's wrong with me in Williston?"

She didn't remind him of the fact that he was in many ways her father's opponent. Instead, she said, "In Williston you're too tense."

"How would you know?"

"I've watched. A one-track mind—the store."

"They pay me to be like that."

"But nobody expects you to cheat yourself of a little fun. I'll bet in all the time you've been in Williston you've never once thought of dancing."

"Well, that's true."

"You ought to take it easier. You'd get a lot more kick out of what you're doing."

He drank a little, put the glass down. "One thing you overlook. I do get a kick out of what I do."

She fixed a searching gaze on his face. He had the same sensation he had known once before—that she was studying him as a subject for a painting.

"The kind of fun and satisfaction," he said, "*you* get out of painting a picture."

"Self-expression?"

He shrugged. "Probably sounds crazy—because you're an artist. Artists, poets, musicians—they see life only in terms of themselves. Long ago somebody told them that all people are divided between the aesthetes and the Philistines. It's a delusion they've never been able to throw off."

She said with mockery, "This begins to sound like the Harvard School of Business Administration."

"No. Just plain fact. You give what's in you to give. In business as in art. Maybe you claim you're doing it for the money——" He gave her a quick, sidelong look. "—or maybe for a block of stock. And up to a point, that's true. Nobody wants to work without pay. *You* don't give a magazine a painting unless they pay. But under it there's something else. A kind of——" He faltered. "Well——"

"Compulsion?"

"Yes! That's it. A compulsion to give everything you've got. In business as in everything else. You're not happy unless you're doing your damnedest. . . . In my own case there's even more to the compulsion."

"In what way?"

"Well, I keep thinking about my father. When he died he had nothing. He was as sweet a guy as ever lived. But for two years after his death I had to pay off debts. It's one of the reasons *I'm* interested in making money and in piling up stock——"

He suddenly realized he had become too serious. The orchestra was playing again. He got up abruptly, held out his hand. "Oh, nuts to all that! Let's dance!"

It was after midnight when they left the Club Caracas. The spring night was warm. Patrice looked up at a full moon and said impulsively, "I want to walk."

So they walked westward on 61st Street till they came to Fifth Avenue and the park. Here a warm breeze met them. Patrice bent against it, holding his arm.

He watched her, surprised and puzzled by the difference in the way he felt toward her in Williston and here. This evening there had been no friction at all.

Unexpectedly she laughed. "Paul, did you ever feel like— like doing something unreasonable? Just for the hell of it?"

"Don't tell me you want to ride one of those horse-and-buggies around the park."

"No, I'm thinking of the other one—the Staten Island ferry."

"You're kidding."

"All my life—" Merriment was a lilt in her voice. "—I've been reading about silly kids who take trips on the Staten Island ferry. I've been up and down the Loire in France. I've taken the boat to Capri. I've crossed the English Channel half a dozen times. I've been loads of places. But never have I been on the Staten Island ferry!"

"Well," Paul said, looking around. "I can be as crazy as the next man." He waved to a taxi. . . .

There were very few people on the ferry at this hour of night. Churning across the bay, it followed the glittering golden lane of the moon's light. They stood on the open portion of the upper deck, where the warm wind blew against them.

Patrice looked back at the towering black mass of New York's skyscrapers. With her hair blowing in the wind and her skirt flapping about her knees, she reminded Paul of a teen-ager.

When the ferry changed its course they walked back slowly so that she could keep the Battery in sight. Seeing the amusement with which Paul was watching her, she said:

"All right, laugh. *I'm* having fun!"

"So am I."

"At a time like this I almost hate to think of going back to Williston."

"Where we don't have fun. At least, not together." A wry grin came to his lips. "In Williston you dislike me."

She stopped. "That's not true."

"Then why do we keep clashing?"

"We don't really——"

"No, we just keep rubbing each other the wrong way."

They leaned against the rail. At the moment Paul found it hard to see Patrice as a source of annoyance. She was a beautiful, wind-blown figure with a small, exquisite face that seemed to shine in the moonlight. They were alone on the deck, halfway across New York Bay. He knew suddenly that he wanted to kiss her. It was illogical, but there was a sense of inevitability about it; the only possible climax for this evening. Useless to try to understand or explain the feeling. He bent toward her.

Patrice withdrew. "No. Don't."

He blinked, wrenched out of the spell. He looked at her in bewilderment. Then he turned away, stung back to clarity of mind. He might have known it. Beneath all the laughter, beneath all the fun, she was still the stiff, unapproachable Patrice Selby. Making a damned production of a kiss.

"I'm sorry," she whispered. "I'm funny that way."

"Forget it," Paul said. "An impulse."

For a long time then she was silent. They heard only the swish of the ferry's rush across the bay. The moonlight glimmered on the waters, and now they were passing the Statue of Liberty.

Patrice said in a low voice, "Beautiful, isn't it?"

"Sure." Of a sudden this whole ferry escapade seemed silly and childish. He should have taken her back to the hotel, and that would have been that.

The queer thing was that in the morning, as he dressed, he was glad he hadn't kissed Patrice. When he remembered the way he had tried, he felt angry with himself. *What the hell got into me?* he thought. *Why should I want to do a thing like that?*

He'd had a few pleasant hours with her at the Club Caracas; even the trip on the ferry boat, when you considered it objectively, hadn't been bad. Why couldn't he accept the whole experience as something of no significance? Why complicate life?

After a hurried breakfast he took a cab to Weller & Dunn's. There he found Martin Traub waiting on the sidewalk. And young Traub was distressed.

"I'm sorry, Mr. Blaze!" he said. "I *tried* to reach you in Williston last night, but you'd already left. Then I called the Barkley a couple of times during the evening. You weren't there, either. When I phoned there this morning you'd already gone——"

"What's wrong?"

"We're too late. Six-thirty last night they closed the deal.

With Renselman's of Boston. Sorry you had to come for nothing——"

If Paul was disappointed, he did not show it. He asked, "How much did Renselman's pay?"

"Thirty-five cents on the dollar."

Paul started up the street, holding Traub's arm, thinking. His eyes were fixed on the sidewalk. "Sixteen hundred suits and 600 coats would have been a big lot for Selby's to handle," he said. "Too big. I figured if *we* landed this deal, I'd call in another store—maybe Christie's in Philadelphia—and offer to cut them in on half of it. They'd have jumped at the chance."

"Anybody would."

"Maybe Renselman's, too, is counting on finding somebody else. Let's get them on the phone. . . ."

Paul called Renselman's in Boston from his hotel. He spoke to Joe Renselman himself. The store's owner admitted, "We *were* figuring on splitting this lot. But you're too late—we've already talked to Crane's in Hartford. They're to make a decision this morning."

"You gave them a definite option?"

"Not an option. An offer——"

"At the price you paid?"

"That's right."

"We're willing to pay 40 cents on the dollar," Paul said. "That will give you an immediate profit of about 14 per cent on half that merchandise before you even move it out of Weller & Dunn's."

Joe Renselman was silent.

"I could have a check on the way to you within ten minutes," Paul added. "Your buyer and ours can split the lot while it's still on the Weller & Dunn floor."

Renselman said, "Can you hold on, Blaze? I want to talk this over."

"Sure."

While he waited Paul calculated. At 40 cents on the dollar, he'd still have an extraordinarily good buy on 800 suits and 300 coats. As for Renselman's, without incurring a penny of overhead they could reap an immediate profit of approximately $2,500. A bonus for quick-action. . . .

Joe Renselman suddenly said, "Blaze?"

"Yes?"

"It's a deal."

Five minutes later, when he hung up, Paul gave Traub a wink. Selby's had what it had wanted—half the Weller & Dunn stock—at a good price. Against competition he might have had to go to 40 cents on the dollar, anyway. Paul said, "Got to start things rolling for a whopping men's clothing sale. . . ."

Chapter
Sixteen

Over breakfast at the Williston Hotel, a week after his trip to New York, Paul was reading the morning paper when a Halliday advertisement all but leaped at him. The coffee cup was raised halfway to his lips. He put it down, spilling a little.

There was a quarter-page box whose copy appeared in formal Spencerian script:

Halliday's

The Center of Fashion

proudly invites you to attend the first showing of originals by Yvette Doré. We particularly call your attention to her latest creation, Tulle de Soir. This distinguished dinner gown is priced at $950. It will be on display throughout the week in our second floor Fashion Salon.

Though it was only twenty minutes past nine when Paul strode into the store, he found Conrad Selby, Ben and Everett already in conference. The morning paper lay open to the Halliday advertisement.

"It can't be accident," Everett was saying. "*Somebody* must have told them!"

Conrad Selby, however, was unperturbed. "I really don't see that it makes much difference. We'd already decided not to go ahead with the idea."

They looked questioningly at Paul as he joined them. Though he was clearly angered by what had happened, he kept the feeling restrained. "After this," he said, "it wouldn't do us any good to go ahead even if we should want to. They've taken the play away from us. The point is—where did the leak come from?"

Selby had a logical explanation. "Halliday's could have picked it up in New York. That's how Randolph Green got it. There's probably been talk around the market."

In any case, speculation was useless. Realizing they had been beaten in this skirmish between stores, Paul went to his own office. And within half an hour Bernardine came in, her expression sardonic.

"I see," she said, "you're now in the business of dreaming up ideas for Halliday's."

"Got to give them a break sometimes."

"I'm sorry you didn't push this notion down the throats of our Board. It was a good idea."

Paul didn't reply. He was tearing open a fresh pack of cigarettes.

"If you like," Bernardine offered, "I'll try to find out who told Halliday's."

"How?"

"I've got a date tonight with Roger Halliday."

Paul gave her a quick glance.

She smiled. "I often go out with Roger. I hope you understand I'm saying this to make you jealous."

"Don't be coy, Berry. On you it doesn't look good."

"All I'm trying to say is I'll do some discreet questioning tonight." She left then, with a characteristic flip of her hand by way of farewell.

Within an hour the incident of the $950 dress had repercussions of a different kind. Perhaps Conrad Selby was contrite about having allowed their chief competitor to seize the lead.

Looking into Paul's door, he asked, "Are you free Saturday night?"

Paul nodded.

"Ben and my daughter Grace are coming to dinner. So is Philip. Like to have you join us."

"Why—thanks. Glad to."

"Seven or so will be fine."

When Selby turned away, Paul was perplexed. Since coming to Williston he had been invited to dinner at Everett's home, at Ben's, at Martha's; all these invitations he had accepted because they gave him opportunities to know the family more intimately. This was the first time, however, that Conrad Selby had asked him. He wondered if Patrice could have initiated the invitation.

He threw the whole thing out of his mind. This was the day the men's clothing sale was to start, and he went down to see how big a crowd the event was attracting. . . .

The following morning Bernardine, wearing a striking blouse-and-skirt combination, came to his office with a dissatisfied expression.

"Roger," she had to confess, "wouldn't talk at all about their $950 dress. Except to kid me for my curiosity."

"I expected that."

"Paul, *I* think Randolph Green must have shot off his mouth."

"You're guessing."

"He was sore, wasn't he?"

"Could be. It no longer matters. We've been beaten to the punch. Period."

But though Paul talked with finality, he was still annoyed.

Saturday night's dinner at the Selby home brought him the same sense of perplexity he had felt on a previous visit. How these people were able to abandon all conversation about their store's problems, he could not understand. Again it made him feel like an outsider.

Over dinner Conrad talked primarily about something called The Granz Memorial Society. Paul had read about it, but his interest had been vague. Apparently its purpose was to bring cultural and artistic enterprises to Williston. He had not known, as he now discovered, that the Selby family was active in its work.

"I believe this year's music series will be the best we've had in a long time," Conrad said. "I've already gone over the program with Martha and her committee. It starts with the Rochester Philharmonic Orchestra in October, then goes on with a piano recital by Myra Hess in November, a cello recital by Piatigorsky in December, the London Male Chorus in——"

Philip interrupted with a smile, "Paul looks puzzled, Con. Maybe we ought to explain."

"This Granz Memorial Society is Dad's personal pride," Patrice said. She managed to fill the words with affection for her father, and a touch of humor. "Before the year's over, he'll nick you for a contribution, Paul. Watch out."

Conrad asked him, "You've heard of Heinrich Granz, haven't you?"

"Composer?"

"A very fine composer, yes. The Philharmonic has played two or three of his works. He lived practically all his life in Williston. When he died—that was seventeen years ago—he left whatever he had, a few thousand, as the nucleus of a fund to bring art, music and literature to Williston. Now some of the town's old families maintain the fund."

Grace mocked, "Oh, Dad, stop being modest!" She added to Paul, "Dad's the leading spirit of the fund. Gives it most of its money."

"That's neither here nor there," Conrad said. "The point is we *do* enrich Williston life. We've brought some of the world's finest artists here."

Patrice said, "Warren Graham recently had an editorial about it."

"Ye-es, I remember that," Paul admitted. "But he didn't mention Selby support."

"Of course not," Conrad said. "We keep that anonymous."

"Why?"

The question seemed to surprise Selby. "Well, it's nothing I specially care to advertise—any more than I advertise other hobbies. Why should I?"

"Seems to me you deserve credit."

"Nonsense." Conrad waved the idea aside with a laugh. "I don't want credit for anything that gives me so much pleasure."

"It could be fine publicity for the store."

There was an instant of silence. Glancing around, Paul

had the impression that it had been the wrong thing to say; he had caused definite embarrassment.

Yet he was confident that the Selbys were overlooking an excellent stroke of public relations. Why not let Williston know that the Selby store took an active part in the community's cultural affairs? It was good business to establish such a reputation.

Philip put in a trifle wryly, "There are some things, Paul, this family doesn't use for publicity purposes."

"I understand. On the other hand——" Paul checked himself. "Are there other community projects the family supports?"

"Well," Ben Lork said, "we contribute to them all, I suppose. But we don't make any to-do over it, if that's what you mean."

"Not even," Philip said, "over the Borden College gifts. Conrad's other pet."

"What's that?" Paul asked.

Conrad scoffed. "That's no *community* project! It's simply a private——"

"It's simply $7,500 a year," Grace interrupted with a laugh.

It was again Patrice who explained. "Borden College is not really part of Williston. But since they established their School of Retailing and Business Administration, Dad's been one of their major supporters."

"A Selby Chair? Something like that?"

"No. Just an annual gift."

Paul started to reply, then left the words unsaid. He still felt like a stranger here. His mind ran in ways altogether different from theirs.

He was thinking suddenly of Edmond C. Christie. Like

Selby, the Philadelphia merchant made a habit of contributing to various cultural activities. His gifts ran into several thousand dollars a year. But every gift was accorded proper newspaper publicity—usually a picture of Christie handing a check to a fund official—and thus Philadelphia was kept aware of the interest the Christie store took in local affairs. Moreover, Paul recalled a local newspaper item concerned with a one thousand dollar donation Brian Halliday had made to an orphanage. Why Conrad Selby should deliberately overlook his opportunities, it was hard to understand. Modesty of that sort was absurd when you were in business.

Paul refrained, however, from mentioning the store again during dinner. Instead he listened to talk concerning the Board of Education's decision to increase teachers' salaries; to the remarkable growth of Pennsylvania as an industrial state; to Williston's plans for a Memorial Day parade.

In fact, they conversed on almost everything except the store. It must have been well after ten o'clock—and they were all in the living room then—before somebody mentioned business. It came indirectly. Grace commented in amusement on the fact that Halliday's was keeping its $950 dress roped off in a corner, and that curious women filed past it in an endless line. So, at any rate, she had heard from friends.

Surprisingly, then, Conrad took the cigar from his mouth and said, "Paul, I must confess you were right about that dress idea. I didn't dream it could cause such a stir."

"Yes, a good hunch," Ben agreed. "The Board shouldn't have undermined it."

"Shows you," Philip remarked as he lit his pipe, "that it's bad policy to toss everything at the Board."

"I never expected this thing to come up at the meeting," Paul said. "The next idea won't. We'll act on it first."

Ben gave him an amused look. "Does that mean the next idea is all ready to go?"

"Just about."

"What is it?"

"Well—maybe we ought not to discuss business now——"

"I'm curious. Let's hear it."

Paul saw that Conrad, too, was attentive. There was no reason to keep things secret. The store would know about it in a few days, anyway, and he had no intention of allowing anybody to scuttle this latest project.

"We're going to run a full-page Selby ad in *The New York Sunday Times*," he said.

They all stared. He might as well have told them he contemplated advertising in Africa.

Philip repeated, *"The New York Times?"*

"That's right. We'll hit a Philadelphia paper, too."

"I—I'm afraid," Philip finally declared, "I'm a bit blind on these things. What would be the point of Selby's advertising in New York? Do you expect New Yorkers to shop in Williston?"

"No." Paul's tones became crisp. He was back on familiar ground. "What I'm interested in is the half-million people who live *between* New York and Williston. Many of them actually live *nearer* Williston than New York. If we convince them they can find the same high-quality goods in Selby's as in the city—and at prices no higher—we could get them to drive our way. Stay out of city traffic. Shop in comfort."

Conrad Selby obviously couldn't agree with this. His face was stern, almost forbidding. "It won't work, Paul. Williston can't pretend to match New York's variety."

"With Selby's and Halliday's here, we offer a good shopping center," Paul insisted. "Besides, there's another value to such advertising. The novelty of it—a Williston store advertising in New York—will make people talk. Matter of fact, I imagine Williston folks will gloat over it. Hometown pride. Their own store. Competing with the New York giants."

Grace suddenly laughed. "Audacious as hell!" she said. "*I love it!*"

Philip inquired, "But what would a scheme like that cost?"

Paul looked at his cigarette. "Frankly, I'm not yet sure *The Times* will accept our ads at department-store rates. We'll probably have to spend about $4,000 a page. But if we can draw even a few hundred customers from other towns, it'll write off the cost."

He saw that Conrad Selby was not convinced.

"The whole idea," he went on, "is to broaden our shopping area. Also, there are twenty-seven weekly newspapers within a hundred miles of Williston. *Their* rates are low. If we advertise in them, there's no reason we can't triple the size of our present buying area."

To Paul's surprise, Ben now came to his support. "It's just wild and impudent enough to catch attention," he said, and his eyes were full of humor. "I take it these ads would not push specific items?"

"No. Institutional copy only. Simply tell what a great store Selby's is, and how easy and comfortable it is to shop for high-quality merchandise by driving to Williston."

The controller nodded. "Be fun to run one and see what happens." And on afterthought he added with a chuckle, "I'd give a lot to see Brian Halliday's face when he reads that ad!"

But Conrad Selby rose, and in the stiffness of his bearing Paul could see opposition. Conrad went toward the record player. Evidently he had decided to end this discussion. Just as clearly, however, he clung to the opinion that New York advertising would be a waste of money. And Paul—with a quick glance at Patrice—knew they were clashing again. . . .

"What all this points up," Conrad said, "is the change that's come over ways of doing business. And I'm not ready to concede my ways are wrong—that I'm an anachronism."

Grace said with affectionate reproach, "Let's not talk it into a big issue."

"But it is a big issue." Conrad started the record player. He watched it, obviously not hearing the music. "I have been trying to analyze the real difference between Paul's point of view and mine. I'm not sure I've struck it, but sometimes I think I catch a glimpse of the truth. It's—the difference between our generations."

"Merely a difference in method," Paul insisted.

"No. Much more. A difference in what we *want*."

Paul sent an uncomfortable glance at Patrice. He had no wish to become involved in a further discussion of philosophies. It could only increase tensions. Yet he could not retreat from the debate.

"In my generation," Conrad said, "we wanted a fair degree of wealth. We wanted respectability. We wanted security. When we built up an enterprise like the Selby store, those were the things we asked of it. And when we got them we felt we were successful. We felt well compensated for our efforts." He gave Paul a sidelong look. "What about your generation?"

"We're not quite that placid," Paul said. "Maybe it's because a couple of wars have given us a taste for excitement— I don't know. But I do know we want something more than security and a sense of respectability. We want—" He paused, searching for the right words. "We want the feeling that we're getting the *most* out of a business—the most out of life." He stopped again, then added, "If there is a difference between generations, it's that mine sees business as a constant challenge. We're not satisfied with a million where we can make two million. We're not satisfied with two million where we can make four—"

"Squeeze the last cent out of everything you do. Is that it?"

"Not the last cent. The ultimate bit of *satisfaction*."

"That means you'll never know a moment of real contentment."

"Maybe not."

"You'll never be happy. No matter how big you become, there will always be the challenge to become bigger."

"Is that bad? Isn't that what keeps life exciting? Stimulating?"

"And exhausting," Conrad said. He lifted the needle off the record. Nobody had been listening to the music. He went back to his chair, again lit the pipe. "I can't help thinking that our family has lived a good life, a pleasant life, with all the comforts we wanted—as long as we lived without reference to the fact that others, like Halliday's, might be doing more business than we were. The minute we became envious, jealous— call it what you like—"

"Competitive?" Paul said.

"All right, competitive. It's what makes us dissatisfied, unhappy. Now I ask you, Paul, how *can* we ever achieve contentment by your methods?"

"I don't know," Paul said. "I'm not even sure contentment is the most important end in life. Contentment is unproductive. The only progress I know comes out of being dissatisfied."

"Yes, but by your standards we'll never know peace. Never. They make for life-long harassment. It's tragic to be so needled by the accomplishments of other men that we never enjoy peace of our own."

"Unless we get around to realizing that competition itself can make life full and happy. We're not just a rocking-chair generation, satisfied to sit on the porch and enjoy what we have."

"Meaning your pleasure comes out of acquiring, not having."

"Could be."

Conrad smoked over this. Nobody else attempted to interrupt. Finally he said, "Ye-es, I can see where that might be possible." He sighed, stared at the pipe. "The question is—don't you eventually want to sit back and rest and try to find out what it's all about? Are we, as a family, living to operate the store? Or do we operate the store so that we may live?"

He gave Paul a thoughtful stare.

"I think we've hit on the answer," he said. "My generation worked to live. Yours lives to work. And we'll probably never find out which is the wiser way. . . ."

Chapter
Seventeen

Two DAYS LATER Paul found Donald Ripley waiting in his office with young Harold Quincey Coombs, the wiry, spectacled decorator responsible for the new display windows. Both men looked so worried that Paul wondered if dissension had risen.

Ripley said, "Mr. Blaze, this is something you've got to hear for yourself! And straight from Harold!"

"What now?"

Young Coombs snatched off his spectacles. "Mr. Blaze, I guess Halliday's know that in order to have our windows match the daily specials, I have to be told ahead of time what those specials are going to be." He frowned at the floor. "Fellow from Halliday's—fellow named Charlie Clay I've played golf with—offered to make it worth my while to keep Halliday's informed. Hundred a week."

It jarred Paul. It was hard to believe. But Coombs' face was earnest. He could have no reason to invent an accusation like this. Paul felt a surge of anger.

Coombs said, "*I* don't play a game two ways. But there might be some who would listen to Clay. They *could* throw Selby's for quite a loss."

Paul said tightly, "Appreciate your telling me this, Coombs. What did you say to Clay?"

"Figured I'd play for time. Till we could talk it over. Told him I wanted a few days to think."

"Good." Paul's lips tightened. He turned from the desk, peering at the window. After a moment he looked at Coombs sharply. "Clay mean anything to you?"

"Not a damn thing."

"Mind if I *tell* him we talked?"

"I've got nothing to lose."

"Okay." When Paul was angry, he generally resorted to direct action. A straight, hard punch, he felt, was quicker and more effective than sparring. He picked up the telephone, told the operator to get him Mr. Clay at the Halliday store.

A minute later he said to the merchandise manager, "Hear you tried to bribe one of our people for advance information on our daily specials."

The direct attack must have staggered Charlie Clay.

"The man you talked to won't give," Paul said. "But there are some who may. So we're going to put a watchdog on duty here—a private detective."

In a constricted voice Charlie Clay said, "What—what in hell are you talking about?"

"If there's a leak here, we'll find it," Paul continued. "We'll give it all the publicity we can. We'll publicly explain how, why, and by whom our co-worker was bribed. That would be lousy publicity for the store that did it."

Suddenly Charlie Clay became outraged. "See here, Blaze, I resent this kind of accusation!" It turned into a tirade. Paul did not interrupt. He took the telephone from his ear, held it so that both Harold Coombs and Donald Ripley could hear. He waited until Clay stopped for breath, then said:

"Nothing'll happen unless I see Halliday's ads start duplicating ours. So from here on in it's your problem, not mine. . . . 'By, Mr. Clay!"

When he put the telephone down, he said, "They won't risk bad publicity. Coombs, I'm damned grateful."

Harold Coombs seemed embarrassed. "Hell, Mr. Blaze, I —I couldn't do anything else."

"We'll show our appreciation."

When Paul told Conrad Selby about it, Selby, too, was shocked. He readily agreed that Coombs deserved a bonus.

"I can't understand Halliday's doing a thing like this," he said. "We've been competitors, but our relations have always been cordial. Brian Halliday and I have served together on many civic boards. We get along fine."

"But now you're stepping on his toes."

"Still. . . . I wonder if Charlie Clay acted without Halliday's knowledge."

"Possibly."

Selby considered this, his fingers playing with his tie.

Paul said bluntly, "I think I put the fear of publicity into Clay. No use pushing it further."

"You're not actually planning to hire a private detective."

"Of course not. The threat's enough."

The brief clash with Halliday's had other repercussions, too. Within half an hour Randolph Green came to Paul's office.

"Say, Mr. Selby just told me how you handled Halliday's," he said. "I think that's swell, Mr. Blaze. They had it coming." Then he became troubled. "There's one thing I ought to tell you. About that $950 dress. I'm not certain, but—*I* might have been responsible for that."

Paul had not expected anything like this. He leaned back, watching Green closely.

"Coming in on the train from New York that day," the buyer said, "I was sore—mostly, I suppose, because I'd been caught off base; didn't know what my own store was doing. Jack Harmon, one of my assistants, was with me. I—I guess I did a bit of beefing. I should have realized Eddie Buchman, of the Halliday store, was sitting right behind us."

Paul let his fingers play with a pencil. He was not disturbed by this admission; rather pleased, in fact, by Green's unexpected candor. He said quietly, "Glad you told me." And then, "Let's forget the whole thing. . . ."

A few minutes after the buyer left Paul stepped out of the office. He was still feeling grateful for the man's frankness when he met Patrice in the executive corridor.

She carried two big boxes. He took them off her hands, and she explained she was merely leaving them with her father. "Some dresses I borrowed out of stock," she said.

He looked at her in wonder.

"For my model," she added. "I had to do six pictures of a bride in various costumes."

Strangely, Paul found himself thinking about that at odd moments throughout the day. It ignited an unexpected idea. . . . He knew, of course, that Patrice resented being used for promotional purposes—she had made that unmistakably clear. On the other hand, this series of a bride in various costumes——

Late in the afternoon he telephoned her. "Patrice, I'd like very much to see those bridal pictures you mentioned."

"Nice of you, Paul. Being polite?"

"When am I ever polite?"

She laughed. "All right. Come over tonight."

He went immediately after dinner, and Patrice led him up to her studio. Following her on the stairs, he was struck again by the slim grace and airiness of her figure. He had a fleeting recollection of the pleasure it had been to dance with her in New York. But also, he remembered the letdown he had felt when she had instinctively drawn back from his kiss. His mouth twisted with cynicism. You had to be careful, he recalled, about what you said or did or even thought with this girl. She took things too damned seriously. . . .

There were fluorescent lights in the studio. Scores of canvasses were stacked against the walls. She took the bridal series up one at a time, set them on the easel. Paul stood a few feet away, eyes narrowed as he studied one after another.

The first was the misty figure of a girl in white bridal lace. The face was soft and glowing. The eyes were filled with joy —as if Patrice had caught her at the instant she saw the groom waiting at the altar.

"These six are supposed to carry the bride through her first summer," Patrice explained. "For the center pages of *Fashion World*."

The second canvas presented the girl in a trim traveling suit, waving good-by from the door of a plane. The third showed her, sylph-like in a yellow swim suit, rushing into a tropical sea. There was one in a white summer dance frock; another in a swirling evening gown; and finally, caught before her vanity mirror, the bride wore flowing pastel-blue lingerie.

"Doggone good," Paul mumbled.

"Thanks. It's the biggest commission I've ever had." Patrice added in deprecation, "Commercial as hell, but I got a kick out of doing them."

"Model a local girl?"

"Yes. A high school senior."

Paul's eyes were still narrowed. He puffed a couple of times at his cigarette.

"The thing's full of local interest," he said. "Local artist, local fashions, local model. How'd you like it if we showed one painting in each Main Street window, together with the Selby dress the model used? We'd pose the mannequin exactly the way you've got the figure on the canvas. It'll be a knockout display."

She stared in amazement.

"What's wrong?" he asked.

"Don't you *ever* think of anything that isn't—promotion?"

"This one is a natural. We'd have to get the magazine's permission, of course. But it's good promotion for them, too."

"Paul," Patrice declared, "I've never met a man like you! If you're not trying to use *me* as a sales gimmick, you're after my work!"

He asked bluntly, "Think the idea is *too* commercial?"

"I don't know. Haven't had a chance to think about it one way or the other."

"Any more commercial to show pictures in store windows than in a magazine?"

"No-o, I suppose not."

"We'd use them at the same time the magazine comes out. Probably get newspaper publicity out of it, too."

To his astonishment, Patrice began to laugh. Her hand went to her throat. She sat down on the square hassock. She tilted back her blond head, and the laughter continued.

"Paul, you're incorrigible!"

He watched in perplexity, not understanding. It could be, he supposed, that she found his promotional pressures ridiculous. Would he *ever* understand how these people thought? . . .

Chapter
Eighteen

THE FULL-PAGE institutional advertisement of the Selby Department Store appeared in *The New York Times* the first Sunday in June:

SELBY'S
—in Williston, Pennsylvania—
One of America's great stores invites you to take a pleasant drive to a city where there are no traffic or parking problems, where you are never rushed, where you can find the highest quality in fashions, housewares, furniture, toys, garden implements or anything else at prices that make a visit worth your while.
SEE SELBY'S!
Everything for Everyone

The effects of the advertisement were prompt. Monday morning Conrad, seated at his desk, had dozens of telephone calls. Most of them were from New York, congratulating the store on its enterprise. A raincoat manufacturer said, "If you're out to make Selby's a national institution, you've certainly picked a good way to begin!" The general reaction was one of good-humored surprise. The ad was apparently conceded to be a startling and provocative gesture. Even Brian Halliday, of all people, telephoned his congratulations, though there was a cutting laugh in his words. Conrad became thoughtful. . . .

And Wednesday afternoon, when Paul came back from lunch, Maud Heller entered his office. There was an odd light in her eyes. She kept her voice low.

"Mr. Blaze, Dr. Gordon Bailey is waiting to see you."

"Who's he?"

"Dean of the School of Business Administration over at Borden College."

"Oh? All right, send him in."

Dr. Gordon Bailey was surprisingly young for the position he held. He could hardly have been more than thirty-five—a brisk, light-haired man with a staccato manner of speech.

"I've come with an invitation," he said.

The following Tuesday, he explained, would be commencement day at Borden. Sixty of the graduates would represent the School of Business Administration, and they would have a class luncheon of their own before graduation.

"I hate to make this request so late," Dean Bailey apologized. "But I'm hoping, Mr. Blaze, you'll be able to be our luncheon speaker. This morning we got word that Senator Wickendon, who was to have come, is sick."

Paul scratched his jaw. Then he toyed with a pencil on the desk. For some reason this struck him as amusing—being asked to address a commencement luncheon.

"Very kind of you," he said. "Seems to me, though, you ought to ask Mr. Selby."

"We've had Mr. Selby in the past." The dean's smile broadened. "What we'd like you to do is talk about your own theories of retailing. And if you want to throw in an explanation of why a store like Selby's advertises in New York City—"

the dean's eyes flickered with merriment "—that'll be fine."

Paul knew that opportunities like this could result in good publicity. They carried the store's name into the news columns. They gave the store a chance to be identified with the community. He accepted. . . .

Bernardine picked up her home telephone and called Paul at the Williston Hotel. This was Saturday evening. "My passport's come," she said. "It gave me a jolt."

"Why a jolt? Should think you'd be pleased."

"Makes my leaving for Paris seem so immediate and—and *rushed*. You realize I'm scheduled to fly just one week from tonight? I'm practically terrified."

"Take it in stride, Berry."

"Sorry, but the blood pressure's 'way up. Isn't it time you gave me a briefing?"

"On what?"

"What firms you want me to see in Paris and so on. How about coming over for dinner?"

"Got to work on inventory reports."

"Knock off for an hour. You've got to eat."

"Well——" He hesitated. "All right. Seven o'clock?"

"I'll look for you."

At the dinner table he discovered that the prospect of going to Paris had brought a glow into Bernardine's face. She looked extraordinarily well tonight, full of eagerness and anticipation.

"First time I'll be out of the country," she said. "You're an angel!" Her hand came across the table to rest on his.

"Forget it." He took a pen from his pocket. "Suppose we jot down some of the firms you ought to see. . . ."

They planned her visits throughout dinner. It was not till they were having coffee that Paul disclosed a new notion.

"Send us a daily cable," he said. "Paris fashion notes. About a hundred words a day. We'll whip it into shape here. We'll run it as a signed box on the fashion pages. Tips from our Paris representative." He grinned. "That'll keep the town awake to the fact that our Fashion Co-ordinator is in Paris."

Bernardine threw back her head and laughed. "You think of more things for me to do than I've ever dreamed of for myself!"

"Don't build it up, kid," he said. "We're doing it because it's good business." He looked at his watch. "Now I've got to get back to those reports——"

"So I'm being ditched. Okay." She rose. "By the way, better make your Borden College talk a knockout. The Selbys have taken a table."

He looked at her in surprise. "What for?"

"To applaud, naturally."

"Who told you?"

"Mr. Selby himself. I've been invited. It's a table for eight."

Paul frowned in irritation. "Oh, nuts! Didn't want this turned into a show!"

"You represent the store, and the owners have a right to be on hand." Bernardine added, "We'll all clap like mad."

It seemed to Paul, when he accompanied Dean Bailey into the dining hall at Borden College, that commencement days were always hot. His own, as he recalled it, had been insuffer-able. He still remembered how the perspiration had streamed down his body under the academic robes.

This day was as bad. Sitting on the dais beside the dean, he faced some two hundred people. Apart from the graduates and their families, there were a good many alumni and faculty members, too.

He nodded to the Selby table. The four women—Patrice, Grace, Bernardine and Mrs. Isabelle Rorich, the head of the store's personnel—were accompanied by Conrad Selby, Ever-ett, Ben and Harry Manderson.

Half a dozen members of the faculty sat on the dais. Their easy fellowship helped allay the nervousness that was gathering in Paul's stomach.

But when the meal ended and the dean rose to rap for attention, the tightness caught him again. Dr. Bailey made a gracious introductory talk, outlining Paul's contributions to the Selby store.

"I'm hoping," he continued, "that Mr. Blaze will give us some of his own ideas on the importance of retailing as a ca-reer. But whatever he says, I'm sure we shall find it of tremen-dous value. . . . Ladies and gentlemen, I am delighted to pre-sent the General Manager of the Selby Department Store, Mr. Paul Blaze."

The applause was polite. It was too hot for any great show of enthusiasm. Rising, Paul acknowledged it with a vague smile, a slight bow. He buttoned the jacket of a light suit; ran a hand over his brown hair.

"That's quite a question the dean brought up—the im-portance of retailing," he said. "Gives me some odd recollec-tions. My ancestry happens to be British. I can still remember the visits my London grandfather used to pay our home outside Boston. He was one of those fine old Victorians, portly and mustached. An editor for a book-publishing house. Wrote poetry on the side. And I can remember how upset he was over the fact that my father had gone into trade. Those were the days when trade was regarded as a second-rate way of life. Especially by the intellectuals. And this was only yesterday—when I myself was a kid.

"Well, times have changed. Nobody sneers at trade any more. There are schools throughout the country—fine schools like this one—which recognize trade, business, commerce, retailing as the important careers they are. Today any man who holds business in contempt ought to have his head examined. We've come to see that few things are more important than the mighty job of keeping the world's economy going.

"What's the retailer's position in all this? How important is it for the retailer to do the right kind of promotion to which Dean Bailey has referred? Well, let me tell you my own feelings."

He paused, looked over the crowd.

"We Americans spend about $130,000,000,000 a year at the retail level. No nation in history has ever come near that kind of spending. It means our people are investing in the best and the most they can get out of life. They're absorbing, using up, $130,000,000,000 worth of merchandise every year.

"Who makes this $130,000,000,000 worth of goods *available* to the public? The retailer. Who distributes it, pushes it? The retailer.

"We may talk about our country's tremendous productivity, about all the things we turn out in greater quantity than any other nation on earth. But this very productivity—the basis of our national wealth—would be bottled up and useless if it were not for the American retailer with the great distributional system he has created."

Paul glanced around the room. Maybe this wasn't a good speech; he was talking simply. But he was dredging out of himself thoughts that were always there, though unspoken. He saw that Patrice was watching him intently. So, for that matter, were most of the others at the Selby table. Only Bernardine avoided his eyes. She was looking at the glass with which her hand played. Perhaps Bernardine was nervous for him. Curiously enough, he himself was at ease now. He spoke without effort, saying things that came of their own accord.

"This process we call sales promotion—I won't deny it's primarily the job of building up your own volume, of stimulating your own profits. But it's something more, too. If, through promotion, you sell 1,000 wrist watches where ordinarily you might have sold only 100—then you have not only brought added benefits into the lives of 900 consumers; you have also created more work for packagers, for distributors, for a hundred others. Promotion at the retail level is a shot in the arm for industry all along the line.

"And promotion isn't merely a matter of advertising. That's a *big* part of it—certainly. But it's just as important to promote confidence in the retailer himself. That is the *highest* form of promotion. Largely it's achieved through sound publicity. A great many people may scorn deliberate efforts to get publicity, but I say that kind of scorn is nonsense.

"There's nothing disgraceful, for example, in a store's engaging in public service programs and letting everybody know it. The store may not at once make money by throwing its weight behind a Community Chest drive. Yet activities like that, by making people talk and think about a store, by making people respect a store, are among the greatest business boosters any retailer can adopt."

He spoke with conviction. He found it easy because this was an intimate chat with people who shared his interests. He sought no dramatic effects. What he gave was his own creed, the reasons he himself had found for respecting the vocation and the methods he had adopted. And since this was the vocation all these graduates too would soon follow, it turned out to be a simple heart-to-heart talk. . . .

When he sat down after fifteen minutes, there was a moment during which no one applauded. The silence, the heat, the attention were intense.

Then, as though someone abruptly realized he was finished, the applause began tentatively. It gathered momentum. Suddenly it was loud and overwhelming. It continued so long that Paul, slightly flustered, had to rise and bow before he sat down again.

He bent toward the dean. "Tried not to talk too long."

"Mr. Blaze," the dean replied, "when you can make these kids proud of the careers they're about to follow, you've said as much as any man can possibly say."

Chapter
Nineteen

An hour later, in his rooms at the Williston Hotel, Paul took a quick shower, got into fresh clothes. When he reached the store, it was almost four o'clock.

Going up by the escalators—which he invariably used because they gave him a chance to stop and see the size of the shopping crowds on every floor—he saw Bernardine in the fashion department. She came to him at once, her eyes bright.

"Paul, that was a good talk," she said. "I've been wanting to tell you how proud I am."

"Thanks, Berry."

"Bet a lot of those Borden graduates come here looking for jobs."

He hadn't thought of that. It suggested new possibilities. He went to his office, gave it consideration. Then he picked up the mouthpiece of the dictating machine.

"Memo to Mrs. Isabelle Rorich, head of personnel," he said. "Please contact Borden graduates who live in towns within a 100-mile radius of Williston. Let's hire as many as we can either for regular jobs or for summer vacation replacements. I'd like them to cover as wide a shopping area as possible. Then ask Everett Selby to place publicity in their local papers—So-and-so joins the Selby organization. The closer ties we establish with these outlying communities, the more people we draw from them. I'll appreciate your co-operation in this matter."

Actually, his basic campaign to broaden Selby's shopping area was progressing well if you judged by the number of charge accounts that were being opened by visitors from other towns. Ben had reported more than 2,000 in the past two months. Since the general upward trend of Selby's business had attracted many new local accounts, too, charge customers now totaled over 30,000. It was a record for the store. And the number was steadily increasing.

As Paul put the dictating machine aside, the telephone rang. It was Patrice.

"Wouldn't you say," she asked, "that the general manager of Selby's—especially on a hot day when he's made an excellent speech—is entitled to quit a bit early?"

He smiled. "It might be arranged. Why, Pat?"

"For a swim out at Hollow Lake."

This kind of cordiality surprised him. It had little precedent. He wondered what Patrice had in mind. . . . Then he looked at his watch. A quarter past four. The talk at Borden College had left him depleted, and the prospect of a swim seemed very alluring.

"Pick you up in half an hour?"

"Fine."

He had never before seen Hollow Lake. There were, indeed, a good many of Williston's attractions to which he was still a stranger. The lake was a surprisingly attractive place. Some two miles wide, its waters sparkled within a circle of low green hills. It offered the only natural swimming facilities near Williston, and during the summer months, Patrice told him,

it was generally crowded. But now, on a mid-week afternoon
in June, Hollow Lake was quiet.

He discovered that Patrice swam with a smooth, tireless
stroke that easily matched the pace of his crawl. They swam
side by side, following the shore line for a couple of hundred
yards before they came out, dripping and breathless and grin-
ning.

No sandy beach bordered Hollow Lake, but there were
innumerable pleasant coves and shaded grassy slopes under
trees. Patrice stretched her slight figure in the shade of an elm.
She clasped her hands under her blond head. Looking up into
the leaves, she seemed content.

Paul lay beside her, propped up on an elbow. His eyes
went over her figure. In the yellow bathing suit, she looked
unbelievably slim and lovely.

"Paul——" She continued to gaze up into the branches.
"While you were talking at that luncheon I—I got the feeling
that I owe you an apology."

"For what?"

"For never really seeing you as you are."

"What would that mean?"

"Well—a man with a—sense of vision about his work.
. . . Maybe that doesn't express it."

"Up to now I was just a guy whose vision was a block of
Selby's stock. Is that it?"

"Something like that."

"You don't have to apologize. It's exactly what I am."

"No."

"I'm working for myself, Pat. Strictly business. Don't get
any illusions." As he spoke he snapped up blades of grass.
"Only, that isn't the kind of thing you say to a graduating
class."

"The things you said, Paul, were the things you meant. I could hear it in the way you spoke. You're like Dad. You've got a deep respect for the job you're doing."

"So what?"

"So I—wanted to tell you I'm sorry I——"

"—had a grubby opinion of me?"

"A wrong opinion."

He looked down at her face. It was faintly drawn, as though even now Patrice was not certain she had said exactly what she had intended to tell him. He still leaned on his elbow, considering her troubled eyes, the straight, sharp line of her nose, the lips that were slightly parted.

What she was trying to tell him, he supposed, was that she had acquired a new respect for him. He stopped tugging at the grass. He let a full minute go by in silence. His eyes never left her face. It began to pull at him again, as it had one night on a ferry. . . .

There was a limit, he learned, to which you could put off a compulsion. He reached that limit now. Bending over deliberately, Paul kissed the parted lips.

This time Patrice did not recoil. Her eyes met his frankly. Maybe she, too, was aware of the inevitability of this kiss.

"That was to say all previous opinions are forgiven," he said.

She gazed up at him, almost expressionless, as if trying to understand what lay in his mind. Then she slowly sat up, shaking back her blond hair.

What amazed him was her calmness. He himself was a bit shaken. He straightened, too, wondering why he felt as if someone had punched him in the stomach.

Patrice said quietly, "So we start on a new basis?"

It alarmed him. What did she mean by a new basis? Did she think that because he had kissed her——

"Don't get me wrong," she said with a smile. "I'm not being romantic. I mean a basis of—better understanding."

"Oh, sure, sure." Paul's voice was short. "Definitely."

"Don't look so scared. You haven't committed yourself to anything by kissing me."

He blinked at her, taken aback by the candor.

"So help me," she said, rising, "never in my life have I seen a man so worried about a kiss."

Paradoxically, it was she who was trying to reduce the incident to something trivial; he who was lending it importance.

Patrice held her hand out to him. "Let's swim back."

She all but pulled him into the lake. Again they swam side by side. When they came out of the water at the bathhouses, she looked up at a clock. It was almost six. She sent him a good-humored glance.

"You weren't planning anything for tonight, were you?"

"Matter of fact, yes. The boys from the TV department are coming to the hotel. To talk over a TV promotion plan."

"Oh——?"

"Sorry. Arranged this yesterday."

"It—doesn't matter." But Patrice's tones were disappointed.

In the morning, when he came to his office, Paul was vaguely exasperated with himself. In kissing Patrice he had let down bars which he had never intended to lower—bars intended to keep his job at the store unaffected by entanglements. Inexplicably, he regarded the kiss as a triumph for her, a defeat for himself. He had in some way surrendered. It put him in bad humor which he found hard to shake off.

He buzzed for Maud Heller. "Ask Bernardine Sorel to come in," he said.

He hadn't slept well. A thousand thoughts had been milling through his mind. In an effort to escape he had concentrated on the store, and at least one constructive notion had come out of the ordeal.

Bernardine, in a sweater and skirt, looked ready to model for the cover picture of a fashion magazine. Yet, when he studied her face closely, he saw that some of its customary glow was missing this morning.

"Sit down, Berry. Got an idea."

"At the lake?"

He shot her a surprised glance. "What would that mean?"

"News spreads fast."

"So what?"

"Nothing."

"Then drop the sarcasm. This is about Paris."

She waited, saying nothing.

"If we hired a designer," Paul said, "could you get her to make up dresses, coats and so on, according to Paris specifications?"

"Certainly."

"We'll open Selby's Paris Shop. A corner in the fashion floor."

Her eyes narrowed.

"Our own exclusive numbers. The latest in Paris styles. You'd head the thing."

"Who'd make up the dresses?"

"I'll take that up with Randolph Green. We'll find a manufacturer."

Her interest increased. "Will Selby's *want* to go into manufacturing?"

"We'll go into anything that boosts volume," Paul said. "The point is: can you handle your end of it? Running the shop?"

"Of course!"

"Okay. That settles that."

He turned back to the papers on his desk. Bernardine rose, clearly excited. Yet something was troubling her, conflicting with the eagerness. She couldn't wrench it out of herself. From the door she looked back at him.

"What—what gives, Paul?"

"What do you mean?"

"You and Patrice."

"Nothing gives!"

She forced a smile. "Know what I'm getting to be? Jealous. Jealous as hell."

This annoyed him. "Don't be silly, Berry."

"Funny," she said. "For the first time I almost regret having to go off to Paris."

He turned to her in anger. "Will you cut it out?"

She continued to regard him in a half-taunting way. "Of course, Paul."

The day Randolph Green returned from his weekly buying trip in New York, Paul summoned him to a conference.

The buyer was nervous. He sat tense, his fingers pattering on the leather arm of the chair. It was hard to understand this perpetual unease in Randolph Green. And yet Paul had found dozens of reasons to admire the man's ability. He was still sending in special buys that were unquestionably a large factor in the steady increase of Selby's volume.

Lighting a cigarette, Paul explained the plan to open a Paris Shop, with exclusive styles, at the rear of the second floor. Whether this pleased Green, it was impossible to tell. He stared impassively at the floor.

"The point is," Paul said, "whatever numbers we run in the Paris Shop will be obtainable at Selby's only. We'll have them specially made up."

"By whom?"

"Find a manufacturer who'll work with us. That's your problem."

Green glanced up with sharpened interest.

"Let the work out on a cost-plus basis," Paul said. "We'll do our own designing. All we ask is workmanship. But damned *good* workmanship. Can you find a shop that'll do it?"

A new light seemed to shine in Green's eyes. "Of course!"

"Here's a chance," Paul said, "to throw something to the old sources you didn't want to drop. Cluss & Hein, for example. Nothing wrong with their workmanship. It's their designs that smell. Think they'd go along on this?"

Green almost rose, but lowered himself again. He looked flushed. "They—they'll go along," he said. "And if you're thinking of coats——"

"Shantz. I know." Paul smiled. "The only stipulation I make is that they quote us a fair price."

"Leave that to me!"

"Think we can get moving by the time Bernardine gets back?"

"You bet!" This time Green did rise. "How much work do you estimate there'll be? They'll want to know."

Paul shrugged. "All depends on how well you and Bernardine push the Paris Shop. Don't make any big promises. Get 'em to come along on a trial basis."

The buyer nodded. When he left, it seemed to Paul that he had suddenly become a man with a purpose.

kissed her. That had been nothing—an impulse, a gesture, no more than a pat on the shoulder.

Was he in her mind, then, because he represented so constant a threat to her father's peace? That could be it. Yes, it *must* be the reason.

Well, it was almost summer, and that was good. Every summer her father took a month's vacation in Canada. He had a small lodge in the Laurentians, on the shores of a lake full of bass; and usually Patrice went there with him. It was where she did most of her landscapes, but she went principally because she didn't want him to be alone.

Until now she had been thinking it would be well for her *father* to get away from the store this year. He would be removed from this unnatural strain; he would have a chance to adjust himself, in peace, to the new situation. Now, for the first time, Patrice began to suspect it would do *her* good, too. She also might profit from a month's absence from Williston. . . .

Paul found Harold Quincey Coombs, the window display specialist, supervising the building of props in the carpentry shop. There was so much hammering that conversation here was impossible. They went into the quiet of Donald Ripley's office.

"You know about the July swim-suit promotion?" Paul asked.

"Only that it's set for just before the Fourth of July week end."

"For five days, right," Paul said. "And I've got a hunch

for the Main Street windows. Let's turn them into a long stretch of beach."

Coombs adjusted his spectacles over questioning eyes.

"Run it the whole length of Main Street," Paul went on. "Get a few loads of white sand for the window floors, and backdrops that show the ocean. In one window a family—mother, father, two kids—all in swim suits, carrying their beach equipment—umbrella, water toys, tubes, lunch baskets. Next window you can have a man asleep in the sand, a newspaper over his face, while his kids bury his legs with their toy shovels. Then three girls running toward the surf. And a window with a group gathered around one of those beach grills, broiling hot dogs——"

As he made suggestions he could see Harold Coombs' eyes brighten behind the glasses. A vision was taking shape: a long stretch of beach, extending from window to window, with people doing the things all people do at the shore, and girls in multicolored swim suits——

"Say," Coombs said, "this will be a *production!*"

Paul agreed. "Let's give it the works."

As he turned away, Coombs remembered something else. "Oh, Mr. Blaze! Today we got *Fashion World's* permission to use Miss Selby's bridal paintings. Same time they come out in the magazine. She said okay, too."

"Fine." That gave Paul an odd feeling of triumph. It was good to know he had at last persuaded Patrice to take some small part in the promotional operations of the store. It was as if he had broken down one element of family resistance. . . .

The beachwear promotion, early in July, proved to be one of the most successful Selby's had ever attempted. For one thing, the window displays, featuring several tons of sand, commanded attention, and the *News* ran a picture of the ex-

Philip wore a short-sleeved sport shirt, and he appeared amused.

"Paul, I almost forgot," he said. "You've got to help me win a ten-cent bet."

Paul asked with a chuckle, "What's in it for me?"

"Half the stakes."

"Okay. You've got yourself a deal."

"This," Philip said, knocking out his pipe against a tree, "concerns a pair of old shoes and one of my patients." He glanced at Patrice. "You remember Mrs. Avery, don't you, Pat?"

"Of course."

"Mrs. Avery was having her attic cleaned out when her maid found the old pair of shoes. Men's shoes that had been bought in Selby's way back in 1907. Never been used. Still in their box, with an old sales slip for $2.95. Mrs. Avery thinks her brother must have bought them just before he died. They have gray cloth tops and black pearl buttons——"

Straightening, Paul became as alert as a hunting dog on a scent. "What's she doing with them?"

"Nothing. I bet her a dime *you* would find some promotional use for the things."

Paul got up, brisk now. "You can collect your dime," he said. "Tell Mrs. Avery that Selby's always refunds the full price of any unused purchase, on demand, and no questions asked. Get her to bring the shoes in, and we'll give her the $2.95."

"Shoes bought in 1907?"

"I wish it were 1807! What's more, Selby's will give her a very nice gift in addition to the $2.95 if she doesn't mind our running a story on the refund."

He knew Patrice was observing him with narrow-eyed

curiosity. After a time, when Philip had gone, she said, "I'm always surprised by the way your mind works. What do you plan to do with these shoes?"

"We'll see."

"Beyond a couple of newspaper paragraphs, what *can* you do?"

"Ask me again after I've had a chance to think about it."

Patrice didn't have to ask. Ten days later a second full-page institutional advertisement appeared in New York and Philadelphia newspapers. This one showed, in full size, a pair of cloth-topped, pearl-button men's shoes, the height of 1907 fashion. Under the picture were the words:

> Selby's Department Store, of Williston, Pennsylvania, has just refunded $2.95—the full original purchase price of these shoes bought in 1907—to Mrs. Althea Avery, a customer who wanted her money back.
>
> Why do we tell you this?
>
> Because it dramatizes Selby's policy of "Money back, no questions asked." That holds true even after half a century!
>
> You can never make a mistake at Selby's for the simple reason that you can always return your purchase.
>
> To escape city traffic, to avoid parking problems, to shop in one of America's truly great stores, try
> Selby's in Williston, Pennsylvania

Patrice read the advertisement on a Sunday morning. She stared in wonder at the full-size picture of the shoes. Because she had been present at the inception of this idea, she felt very close to it—almost as if she had sat inside Paul Blaze's mind, watching the wheels whirl. And she was strangely excited. This was an effective advertisement. Good public relations. She could not see how even her father might object to such a thing —yet in the very speculation she had an uncomfortable feeling of disloyalty. For Conrad Selby, she realized, this must be merely an additional indication that all initiative had been wrested away from him. . . .

The morning she and Conrad left for Canada, most of the store's Board of Directors came to the station to see them off. Paul was there too—a trim figure in a light summer suit. He shook hands with Conrad, and with Patrice.

There were a good many people around them. Nevertheless Patrice, stepping close, managed to whisper, "Please, Paul, don't turn things inside out while we're gone. Leave *something* Dad can recognize as his own!"

He looked straight into her eyes, and his smile faded. He resented this implication that with Conrad Selby away he intended to run amuck. He said, "I'll do the job as I see it, Pat."

Chapter
Twenty-One

DURING AUGUST, while Conrad and Patrice were away, Paul discovered that he could get along surprisingly well with Ben Lork. Though the controller kept a close check on everything that occurred, he offered few objections to Paul's methods.

Toward the middle of the month, however, he received a letter that quoted prices for the use of a helicopter. It began, "Referring to your inquiry of August 10th——" Because it had to do with costs, the note came to Ben's desk. Puzzled by it, he went along the corridor to consult the general manager.

"Say, Paul, what's this about a helicopter?" he asked.

"Oh, that. Christmas promotion. I'm trying to get it nailed down early."

"A *helicopter?*"

Paul smiled. "The idea," he said, "is to have Santa Claus flown in, circling all over town. Then we'll have him leave the helicopter by a rope ladder and come down on Selby's roof."

"You're kidding."

"Not at all. We'll dress a stunt man in a Santa Claus suit. Give the event plenty of advance publicity. I'll bet the streets around Selby's will be jammed with kids and their parents. It'll be the talk of the town."

Ben's face became grave. He stared at the letter, then shook his head. "No dice, Paul. I can't go along with that."

"Why not?"

"Sounds like—well, like something better suited to an amusement park."

"Santa Claus is for the kids," Paul argued. "I think the kids will go for it in a big way."

Ben became solemn. His voice sank. "Paul, I've been trying to go along lately with every notion you've had. But this one—I'm sorry. It's exactly the kind of circus stunt I fought against from the beginning. Lacks the dignity we want to keep for the Selby store."

"Will you still say that if we double our Christmas toy sales?"

"I'll still say that no matter what happens. Flying Santa Claus in by helicopter strikes me as—hell, like making a joke and a spectacle of the whole Christmas season. People in Williston are sensitive about things like that."

"Well, look," Paul said. "This is only August. We don't have to argue over it now. Why don't you leave it to me?"

"I'm just saying——"

"I know, Ben. You don't like it. Okay. Let me do the worrying over this one."

It was the only time they discussed it during Conrad's absence. Possibly Ben felt the idea had been dropped after his objection, because his normal spirits were soon restored—perhaps by the fact that summer business retained a high level.

Paul, however, did not forget the conversation. It made him foresee a serious Christmas struggle. . . .

Conrad and Patrice returned from their vacation soon after Labor Day, and the following morning the tall, gray-haired president of Selby's accompanied his general manager on a tour of the store. It proved to be an unsettling experience; in some ways a harrowing experience.

For Conrad saw too much that was unfamiliar. The interior displays had undergone changes in practically every department. As he went from floor to floor with Paul, he felt like a stranger who had been away for years.

There was, for example, the new Paris Shop. He halted, stared—seeing a corner of the fashion floor which had been completely rebuilt. Its walls had murals depicting the Place de la Concorde, with the Champs Élysées running off to the distant Arc de Triomphe, barely visible a mile or so away.

Bernardine, beautifully sun-tanned, came to greet him with a bright smile and a warm handclasp. "Welcome back, Mr. Selby!" She waved to the shop. "How do you like it?"

"Very impressive," he had to admit. As he blinked at the smartly dressed mannequins, he saw Paul and Bernardine exchange the glance of two people who had accomplished something spectacular. "How's it doing?" he asked.

"Better than I'd dared hope," Bernardine answered. "We may hit $200,000 this first year."

"That so? But production costs must be pretty high on those exclusive models——"

"Oh, we've licked that."

"Ben started to tell me last night, but we were interrupted." Conrad turned questioningly to his general manager. In a light gray suit, Paul too looked as if he had spent a good deal of August in the sun—though, actually, he had allowed himself only Sundays for recreation.

"Matter of fact," Paul explained, "all we did was pick

three other department stores around the country—one in Texas, one in California, one in Boston. It took a few weeks of negotiation, but we put it over. They've all installed Paris Shops like ours. The four of us now use the same exclusive numbers. So quantity production has cut costs considerably."

Selby was thoughtful as he walked on.

The daily specials too, he saw, were still attracting crowds. As a matter of truth, things seemed to be flourishing in every department.

On the main floor he looked in surprise at a small counter, rolled along on wheels, on its way toward a Main Street exit. It was laden with plastic raincoats and umbrellas, and he remembered it had begun to rain when he'd arrived.

"One of our new movable displays," Paul said. "Something we've been trying out the past few weeks. In bad weather, for instance, we roll raincoats and umbrellas to the front so they'll be the last thing people see before going out into the rain. Did good business last time."

Selby watched until the display was properly settled near the door. "Been using portable counters for—anything else?" he asked.

"Oh, yes. Several things. For example, we ran a special men's shirt sale last week. And among the shirt counters we rolled one of these portables piled high with women's hosiery, another loaded with women's gloves. A sign on each said 'Be nice to yourself, but remember her, too.' " Paul smiled at the recollection. "I guess when a man spends fifteen or twenty dollars on himself, he feels a bit guilty. Thinks maybe he ought to spend a couple of bucks on his wife, too. So when he sees a feminine display handy right next to the shirts he's just bought . . . Well, the two portable counters, hosiery and gloves, ran up an $800 day. . . . Next time we'll try the reverse: men's socks, ties, handkerchiefs, and so on in the women's department during fashion sales."

All this was so foreign to the things Selby's used to do that its president found himself accompanying Paul in an increasing daze. After the tour, as he went toward his own office, Everett stopped him in the executive corridor. And Everett was enthusiastic.

"Hope you like the way things are humming," he said.

"They—they're humming, all right," Conrad granted.

"It'll be a year that builds up to a promotional climax at Christmas. Paul tell you about the helicopter idea?"

Conrad's eyes widened. "Helicopter idea?"

So, laughing with the contemplation of the Santa Claus spectacle, Everett outlined it. Obviously he felt it would be effective. But Conrad, though he concealed it, was appalled. He recoiled from the plan. . . .

Alone in his office, he sat down to think. With his elbows on the arms of his chair, Selby made an arch of his fingertips. He stared intently at the wall.

Though he was somewhat pale now, he looked well. The month in Canada had left him rested and clear minded, and he could view things with new perspective.

A helicopter . . . but he pushed that aside. It was only one part of a pattern. . . . Only a fool, he told himself, would deny that Paul Blaze was having remarkable success. Dollars were the proof. Yet Conrad could find no satisfaction in what he had found. All this reminded him too keenly of the Humphrey Lascot incident. . . .

Humphrey Lascot was a middle-aged novelist who owned a summer cabin on the same Canadian lake to which Conrad went. Through the years they had become fairly close friends. And a couple of weeks ago Conrad and Patrice had driven into

Three Rivers with Lascot to see a new motion picture based on one of his novels.

Conrad had found it an engrossing picture—taut, moving, extremely well acted. True, it bore only a remote resemblance to the book from which it had been adapted; the screen writers had taken incredible liberties. But what they had produced, Conrad secretly felt, was infinitely better than Humphrey Lascot's leisurely and somewhat obvious plot.

Coming out of the theater, Conrad had said with complete honesty, "It's excellent, Humph! Congratulations. It held me every second."

To his surprise, Lascot had merely grunted. And when Patrice had squeezed his arm, Conrad had turned to see that Lascot's expression was bitter and disillusioned, and his eyes were filled with cynicism.

"I don't care how good it is," Lascot had said. "It isn't *mine.* . . ."

Now, sitting at his desk, Conrad Selby could understand exactly how Lascot had felt. The store, too, was good; but it was no longer his own. It bore the mark of Paul's personality, not of Selby's. Like this crazy helicopter plan. The changes that were taking place were the measure of his own loss, he told himself.

Yet it need not be a loss. He sat up stiffly, took a cigar from his pocket. He frowned as he lit it. The final decision could still be his, and he intended to seize it.

As he tossed the match into a tray, his son-in-law came into the office. Ben was brisk and in good spirits.

"How do you like it?" he asked.

Selby said impassively, "Quite a few things seem to have happened around here while I was away."

Ben grinned. "They sure have! Things are going well."

"*How* well, Ben?"

"At this rate we should hit somewhere between seven and eight million this year."

Selby nodded. "Very good." After a moment he got up. His manner changed. "You and Grace free Sunday night?"

"Far as I know, yes."

"Come over to the house. I'll call the others. I want a stockholders' conference."

Ben eyed him curiously. "Something wrong?"

Conrad Selby said only, "There's a matter I've got to discuss with you all. . . ."

Sunday evening, contemplating the family group in the living room, Patrice thought it a pity that they gathered so seldom. Some had their idiosyncrasies—Mark Reickert, for example, with his rough, hard-driving ways. But fundamentally they were a decent lot. She liked them. Each in his own way had reached a respectable level of achievement. She sat on the couch, smoking a cigarette, looking about at them with a pleasant sense of possession.

"Something's come up which I'd like you all to think about," Conrad Selby said, glancing from face to face. "It started some months ago at an NRDGA meeting in New York. At the time Stephen Wolcott talked to me."

They had all heard of Wolcott. A major figure in the department store industry, he directed the destinies of twenty-three huge stores throughout the country.

"The Wolcott chain is expanding," Selby continued. "Adding a dozen outlets next year. This summer Wolcott came to see me in Canada to continue negotiations. . . . The Wolcott chain wants to buy Selby's."

The fact that someone had made an offer for the store was not surprising. Such offers had come at various times in the past. What *was* astounding was the fact that Conrad Selby appeared to be giving it serious consideration. Never before had he done that. The store was his birthright, his heritage, and in the past he would as soon have sold it as sell a part of his body.

Mark Reickert said with some uneasiness, "You—you turned the bid down, didn't you, Con?"

"I did nothing," Selby answered. "I simply agreed to pass the offer along to the other stockholders."

Martha asked quickly, "Did Mr. Wolcott stipulate a price?"

"That's to be based on the store's business at the time the transaction is arranged."

"Meaning," Martha pressed, "that every dollar Paul now adds to our volume increases the price?"

"Exactly."

Mark bent forward in amazement. "Con, are you saying you *want* to sell?"

"I have an open mind on the subject."

"*I* can't see why we even consider it!" Mark declared.

"On the contrary, I think it's well worth considering."

Dr. Philip Selby smiled as he tamped tobacco down in his pipe. It was a wan smile, almost sad in its understanding. No doubt Philip guessed that Conrad Selby felt *he* had already lost the store. Its control had been out of his hands ever since Paul Blaze had arrived. What difference did it make, then, if it were operated by a Paul Blaze or a Stephen Wolcott?

Martha, her face flushed, asked, "What—what sort of deal would this be, Con? Cash?"

"There'd be only a part cash settlement. For the rest—on an exchange of stock, all of us would get a proportionate share of stock in the Wolcott Corporation." He paused, glanced at Ben and Everett. "Naturally, I made certain stipulations. I said we would not consider any deal in which Ben did not continue his position as controller of the store—at either his present salary or better—and the same, of course, goes for Everett. Wolcott has no objection to that kind of arrangement. In fact, he *wants* the store to be run by local personnel."

Philip inquired, "What about you, Con?"

With a vague smile Selby shook his head. "My position doesn't matter much now. I—I'll retire." He drew a long breath, looked toward a window. "I'm almost sixty-three. Maybe it's *time* I saw a little of the world."

Mark Reickert, angry and resentful, pushed his heavy figure out of the chair. "This is ridiculous! No reason in the world we should sell out now! For the first time in years we're really going places!"

"You're wrong," Selby said. "At a time like this, when we're on the upgrade, we can get the best price."

"But we don't *want* to sell! If the store is valuable to Wolcott's, it's just as valuable to us!"

It became apparent to Conrad, as he looked around at uneasy expressions, that most of the others also were recoiling from the idea.

Ben declared, "I see no advantage in giving up our present independence. We're in a sound position. We don't need the backing of a chain."

"Doesn't make any sense to me, either," Everett said. "If

business is going to boom, let it boom for us, not for Wolcott's."

Only Martha seemed to find the prospect exciting. Her eyes were bright. It was as if Conrad had suddenly opened visions of unexpected wealth.

He went on, "Wolcott has asked that we make up our minds by the end of the year. I'm putting it to you now so that you can give it thought. We can discuss it again some other time."

Mark Reickert said harshly, "Look, Con, you're not going to let the news of this nonsense get out to the co-workers, are you? My God, that's the worst thing you could do to the store —spread the rumor that it's up for sale! Kill the morale of the whole sales force!"

"I quite agree," Selby said. "I count on all of you to keep this confidential."

Everett asked abruptly, "What about Paul? *He's* entitled to know."

"I don't see why."

"He's got a potential stock interest——"

"His contract will be protected."

"How?"

"That's something we can discuss with Wolcott at the proper time."

Grace put in, "Dad, Everett's right. I too think Paul should be told what's in the wind. Seems to me the general manager is entitled to that."

Selby raised his brows. There was no sense making an issue of something which didn't matter. "Very well," he said. "If you all feel that way, I'll tell him."

Chapter
Twenty-Two

THAT EVENING Mark Reickert reached his home in Medill in a mood of seething resentment. He mixed himself a long drink of bourbon and water, gulped it down as if it were medicine, shuddered at its taste. With the glass in his hand, he caught a glimpse of his reflection in a mirror. His heavy face seemed puffed. There were bags under the eyes.

Going to the window, he looked out into the darkness. He was determined to fight against this idea of selling Selby's to the Wolcott chain. No doubt there could be financial profit in the transaction. But he had no interest in becoming a Wolcott stockholder. If new ownership took over the Selby store, Mark would have to give up the dream that had so long glowed in him—the impudent, magnificent dream of becoming Selby's chairman of the Board. Once Wolcott's began to dictate the destiny of the store, there would be no Board of Directors at all at Selby's. All decisions, he knew, would be made by the parent organization in New York.

Mark swung around from the window. His eyes smouldered. There were ways of preventing this, he assured himself. Just a matter of marshaling enough stockholders' votes.

He knew how Conrad would vote. But tonight he had

developed qualms about Martha—though why on earth *she* should want to see the sale consummated, Mark could not understand. What had got into the woman? He'd have to talk to her, make her see that she could earn just as much money— maybe a great deal more—by voting to maintain the store's independent status.

As for Philip—Mark had never been able to cope with the doctor. He could not understand how Philip might react to any given situation. At the meeting Philip had offered no indication of his intentions.

Well, Mark thought, he'd certainly have to do *something* about the threat of a sale. Damned soon, too. No use letting the project gather momentum. . . .

Martha went to bed as soon as she reached home—but she lay awake in the darkness, her eyes wide open and bright.

What Conrad had revealed struck her as a possible windfall. Who could say how much cash this deal might entail? Not that she expected to receive all of eighty thousand dollars. No, nothing like that. Still, there should be a sizable amount. That might mean she'd have no need to borrow too heavily for Jerry.

She felt wonderful about everything that was happening —so wonderful that she wanted to share her joy. Though it was almost midnight, she sat up, switched on the bedside light. She picked up the telephone and called Jerry's number in New York.

After a time she could hear the buzz. She knew Jerry needed the assurance she could give him. Once he was certain that in a few months there would be enough to finance his play, Jerry would throw off the moodiness that had overcome him in recent weeks. He'd be himself again. Gay, laughing, full of affection. . . .

The operator said, "Sorry, ma'am. There's no answer. Shall we try again later?"

Martha felt let down. She looked at the clock. "No, never mind, thank you."

As she put the telephone aside a pang of doubt shot through her. Where *was* Jerry? What did he do night after night when there was no answer in his apartment? . . . These were questions about which Martha did not like to think. She tried purposefully to thrust them out of her mind. Switching off the light, she lay down again.

She waited an hour. During that hour she thought about Jerry, about the sale of the store, about a thousand things— and still sleep would not come.

With a pang of conscience she considered Everett. Would she be betraying her son by agreeing to the sale of the store? No, not really. Conrad had assured them that Everett's position and income would continue.

True, Everett would never be president; but deep within herself Martha felt that the presidency would ultimately have gone to Ben, anyhow. Ben was older, more experienced, Conrad's heir-apparent. Yes, the chances were, under the present regime, that Ben would be elected. And she had no reason to sacrifice a single shred of her own happiness for Ben.

Abruptly Martha opened the bedside cabinet and fumbled for a sleeping pill.

Always, before going to bed, Dr. Philip Selby lit a final pipe and read for a half-hour. Tonight, however, his book lay forgotten in his lap. He stared at the carpet.

It seemed to him that if the Selby store were sold, it would to some degree mean a shattering of the Selby family itself. What else bound them together as tightly as the big gray building on Main Street? The truth was, he realized, Mark, Martha and Conrad had very little in common outside the store. Even now, Conrad and Mark seldom saw each other between Board meetings.

But beyond a business reason for getting together at regular intervals, something precious would be lost. Philip saw the store as more than a family bond. It was, in a sense, an altar to which the family's lives had been dedicated.

Yet he perceived a certain bitter logic in Conrad's willingness to sell. Conrad had poured his life into the store. If now, in his late years, it brought him chagrin and disappointment and pain, why cling to it? By hiring Paul Blaze, the other members of the Board had long ago turned the store into a symbol of Conrad's failure. Philip could well understand that a proud and sensitive man would wish to cut loose from such a symbol of his rejection.

Retirement, Conrad had said. Travel. Often Philip thought of it himself. If that was what Conrad most wished, why not let him have it? Certainly he had earned a period of ease after more than forty years of work in the store.

The trouble lay in the problem of Everett and Ben. How fair was it to the next generation for this one to sell its birthright? There were strange ethics involved, and Philip was not yet sure what he would do if the matter came to a vote. His uncertainty lay in the fact that he was fond of them *all*. . . .

Ben and Grace, having left with Everett and Betty, stopped at their house for a nightcap. The two men took their drinks into Everett's den.

"Hell of a note!" Everett snapped.

Ben said quietly, "It won't happen. It can't."

"I wouldn't take any bets! When my uncle gets a notion, he can be damn stubborn."

"It's your mother who puzzles me. Why does she want to sell out?"

Everett said, "Search me. I'll have to take Mother in hand. . . ." And then, "Ben, suppose the deal *were* to go through? Where would that leave you and me?"

Ben laughed without humor. "You heard what'll happen: We'll be 'taken care of.'"

"Nuts to that! You don't want to work for Wolcott's any more than I do!"

Ben stared down at his liquor. "No. And Mark certainly won't vote for it. I don't know about Phil." He glanced up at Everett. "In the end it may all depend on which way your mother goes."

Everett was about to say he felt certain his mother could be persuaded to vote for his future, to vote in a way that would give him a chance to become president of Selby's. This, however, was the one thing he did not care to say to Ben. He put his glass aside.

"What I've got to make Mother understand—and you can help me with figures—is that she's got most to gain by keeping the store in the family."

"Won't be hard to prove. The way things are going, our dividends ought to be considerably higher than they were last year."

"How would that compare with what she'd be likely to get out of Wolcott's?"

"If I remember, Wolcott stock paid 2¼ per cent last year. We'll do better."

"What—what interested Mother seemed to be a chance of raising quick cash." Everett frowned, ran a hand over his jaw. "Wonder why. She doesn't *need* it."

Ben said dryly, "You work on her, Ev. I'll take on Philip. We can stop this thing." As he rose, he uttered a brief laugh. "Funny. I just okayed funds for this year's Anniversary Banquet. Some affair it'll be if the co-workers learn it may be the last. . . ."

Chapter
Twenty-Three

Paul heard about the contemplated sale just before he was scheduled to meet with the store's buying staff. The shock of the news made him face Conrad Selby incredulously; it caught him wholly unprepared.

At that instant Maud Heller came into his office to say, "They're waiting for you in the conference room, Mr. Blaze."

So there was no time to speak to Conrad with any degree of reason and calmness. At this meeting general plans for Christmas promotions were to be laid out—a matter too urgent to be postponed. Most of the buyers had come in from New York for the conference. And though he was shocked by Selby's news, Paul had to leave him.

The meeting began at four. By the time it ended, after five, he found that Selby had gone home.

He felt harried when he went into his own office. Bernardine was waiting, and she gave him a searching scrutiny. "You look beat," she said. "What's the matter?"

He sat down, ran stiff fingers through his hair, reached for a cigarette. "Nothing. What's on your mind, Berry?"

"Mostly you. You walked into that meeting like a ghost.

And you don't look much better now. . . . Anything *I* can do?"

"No." His fingertips drummed impatiently on the desk. Selby had asked him not to mention the sale, and he could see the wisdom of silence. "No, Berry, nothing at all."

"Couple of things I *should* talk to you about. Only, you don't look in the mood. Maybe tonight——" She paused. "I'm fixing a cool supper. That's an invitation."

He gave her a forced smile. He was about to refuse—and then he knew he didn't want to be alone; didn't want to brood over having the ground cut from under him. He said abruptly, "Sounds fine, Berry. Thanks. I'll be there. . . ."

Her apartment was warm. While she worked in the kitchen he threw off his jacket, opened his collar, lay down on the long, modern couch. With his hands clasped under his head, he stared at the ceiling.

There was no use fooling himself. He had no desire to pour out his heart and his energy for the Wolcott Corporation. If they bought Selby's, he might as well quit.

As general manager of an independent store you could follow your own judgment. You were boss. You used your initiative; you enjoyed flexibility of decision; you shaped your own future. But once you became a puppet in a chain like Wolcott Stores, you did what you were told by a management board in New York. They bought for you, they set your prices, they established your policies, they even decorated your windows. . . .

While Selby's remained independent, it was easy to dream of some day owning a substantial share of the store, but he could hardly have that kind of dream about the Wolcott Corporation. At best he'd be another of ten thousand stockholders. . . .

Funny, he thought, looking at the ceiling. Funny as hell. By his very success in sales promotion he was shattering the goal he most wanted. The bigger Selby's volume now grew, the more determined Wolcott's would be to acquire the store.

Could it be that this was why Conrad Selby's attitude had changed in recent months? No doubt Selby had long known about the offer.

That was how Bernardine found him when she came in to set the table—smiling at the ceiling in bitter understanding.

She made no comment. When the food was down, she waved to it with a casual gesture. "Come and get it."

It was a pleasant meal for a hot September night. It helped to restore Paul's spirits. He finally leaned back from the table.

"Sorry, Berry. Didn't mean to go sour. . . . What was it you wanted to talk about?"

"It can wait."

"No. Let's have it."

"Well——" She was stirring sugar in her iced coffee. "Paul —there's something I picked up in New York. I don't *like* to speak about it. On the other hand, you ought to know."

This was a tone he rarely heard in Bernardine—hesitant. He studied her curiously. Ever since the opening of the Paris Shop she had spent at least one day a week in New York. You had to keep in constant touch with the American branches of French couturiers.

She said, "In spite of lower costs—on the French numbers we're having made up for the Paris Shop we're overpaying almost a dollar a garment. So are the other stores. Because they rely on us."

"Impossible," Paul said. "Ben checks every bill."

"The *bills* are all right. We take our loss on what Cluss & Hein charge to make up a dress; on what Shantz charges to

make up a coat. I've checked with half a dozen other manufacturers, Paul. Showed them samples. Got their bids. I tell you
I can have the Paris line made up at a dollar a garment under
the price Randolph Green is paying."

Paul's eyes narrowed. "Green's a good man," he said. "He
wouldn't let himself be played for a sucker."

"*You* figure it out."

Paul raised his coffee, sipped it. His eyes remained fixed on
Bernardine. "Think Green's getting kickbacks, do you?"

"All I know," she repeated, "is that *I* can get the same
work done at a better price."

An amused flicker came into Paul's eyes. "Berry, are you
by any chance gunning for Green's job?"

To this she did not reply.

"Things begin to add up," Paul said. "The time you
showed me the order he placed with Cluss & Hein——"

"Paul," she broke in, "I'm on the Board of Directors. I
don't want to see the store gypped!"

"Am I wrong about Green's job?"

Bernardine deliberately put down the glass. "All right, so
I want to get ahead."

"It would take an awful lot to make me shove a man
like Green aside, Berry. He knows his business. And so far you
haven't proved a thing against him."

"Ask him why he's overpaying."

"What do you expect him to answer?"

"Ask him why he doesn't go to other manufacturers!"

"Okay," Paul agreed. "I will. If you're sure of your figures."

"I'll have them on your desk in the morning." Bernardine rose. Her thumbs hiked up the belt of her skirt as she went
to the window. He had the impression that her whole body was

tense. As he contemplated her through the smoke of his cigarette, he recognized her driving ambition more clearly than ever before.

Not that he blamed her. Who wanted to stand still? And in the Selby organization the next step upward from Fashion Coordinator would be head buyer. It was a job to which she could not aspire, however, as long as Randolph Green held it. . . .

Rubbing out the cigarette, he rose from the table and went to stretch himself on the couch. "Why don't you quit sniping? You can leave Green to me."

Bernardine drew a deep breath, then began taking dishes into the kitchen. And Paul lay thinking. The possibility of the store being sold still darkened his mood, so that nothing else seemed very important, not even Bernardine's complaints.

When she joined him again she had regained some of her normal good humor. She switched on the television. She made Paul move his lean body over on the couch and she sat beside him, watching the TV screen.

Half an hour later, when the program was over, she glanced down at his face. A slow smile came to her lips. "You look a lot better."

"Let's say you're the restful kind," he answered with a grin.

"I *am* good for you."

"Wouldn't be surprised."

"I ought to make you marry me. For your health."

He said nothing to that; he didn't even think Bernardine was serious.

She added, "Before somebody else gets you."

"Baby," he said, "I plan to go on being single a long, long time. I'm a lost cause."

She got up, crossed the room to seek another program on the TV screen. When she found something she wanted, she swung around.

"I'll be damned," she said, "if I know why I let you kick my pride around. I practically propose, and you turn me down. I wouldn't take it from any other man!"

Chapter
Twenty-Four

To Everett the argumentative evening he spent with his mother brought only despair. For an hour he tried to make her understand the folly of selling out to the Wolcott Corporation. He walked back and forth in her living room, all but pleading. It did little good.

Martha, with a remote expression, listened patiently. Now and then, when he made a reasonable point, she even nodded. But Everett could see that he hadn't changed her basic disposition to follow Conrad's lead.

"I don't get it, Mibs," he said. "*Why* do you want this deal?"

He had asked this so often that she knew she had put him off as long as she could. After all, this giant with the crew-cut hair was no longer a child. He demanded and deserved intelligent answers. Yet Martha knew she could not tell him the complete truth. On the other hand, she couldn't simply sit silent, refusing to reveal anything at all.

"Ev," she said, "I'm trying to raise some money."

That stopped him. "What for?"

"I want to back a play.'"

He blinked. She might as well have told him she wanted to finance a polar expedition.

"A—a play?" he repeated.

"A very good play."

"I don't get . . . *whose* play?"

There had to be limits to frankness. Martha said, "It—it's a play Ralph Crossley is planning to produce. You've heard of Ralph Crossley?"

He could only stare.

"I know him quite well," she said. "I've read the play a dozen times, and I think it's a smash. I've promised to put money into it."

Everett sat down as if his knees had buckled. "Mibs, this—this throws me. You'd sell out Selby's to—*back a play?* I can't believe it!"

Martha reached for the silver coffeepot, poured herself another cup. Perhaps, she thought unhappily, she had already said too much.

Everett protested. "For God's sake, Mibs, have you lost your mind?"

"A good many people back plays without being accused of going mad." Her eyes flashed in sudden rebellion. She said sharply, "All my life I've done the amiable, conventional thing. What's wrong in once following my own desires?"

"Who—who wrote this play?"

"You wouldn't know him."

"Good Lord, Mibs—you're going to risk your money on some *unknown's* play?"

Martha felt trapped. She sought some way of escaping, and there was none. All she could do was put Everett on the defensive.

She said, "You think I'm throwing away your chance to

be president of Selby's, don't you? Well, I'm not. I'm convinced we couldn't swing enough votes to defeat Ben. So I'm not harming you at all. . . . Now let me pour you coffee. I'm tired of this discussion. For once, Everett, I'm determined to go my own way!"

Ben Lork, lean and red-haired, slowly puffed a cigar as he watched his father-in-law. Conrad Selby was selecting Toscanini recordings to place on the record player.

They were alone. Patrice had taken Grace up to the studio. And Ben reverted to the subject that never left his mind these days.

"Any way you look at it," he said, "this sale to Wolcott's would be a bad deal."

Selby continued to read the labels on records. "Nonsense," he answered. "You'll all make just as much money—probably more."

"It isn't a question of money."

Over his shoulder Selby sent Ben a confident smile. "Position? I'm not worried about that, either. I have a hunch you'll go far in the Wolcott organization."

"I'm not interested in the Wolcott organization."

Selby's expression changed. Turning, he suddenly looked old and worn and haggard. "You—you think *I* like giving up the store?"

"No. I realize you're doing it in resentment. But you're not hitting back at the Board by doing this. You're hitting back at the family."

"The family will be just as well off with Wolcott stock as

with Selby stock. The one thing everybody overlooks is that the Wolcott chain is one of the strongest in the country."

"That may be true. But don't sell family sentiment short."

Selby forgot the record in his hand. "Look at the other family-owned stores Wolcott's have bought," he said. "Bigger stores than ours. Older, too. Rancey's in St. Louis. Hale & Bradford in Detroit. Willcox's in Richmond. You think all those families were stupid? Think they all made mistakes?"

"No-o, but——"

"I've talked to them. Not a single one regrets joining the Wolcott chain. Not one lost anything by the deal. You realize what it will do to our buying power?" Selby sat down, bent toward Ben. "The Wolcott chain, last year, did a total of over $400,000,000! There's no disgrace in joining an organization like that!"

Ben looked at his cigarette. "Trying to convince me or yourself?"

Selby stared. Then he got up and went to put on the record.

"I've got to follow my own judgment," he said.

Day after day the feeling of depression, of being defeated by circumstance, grew heavier on Paul. He made his rounds of the store as he always had. His eyes darted about, seeking ideas. But now few ideas came. It was hard to be energetic in a lost cause. Everett had assured him, somewhat glumly, that Conrad and Martha, joined by Philip, controlled enough stock to vote the sale of the store. Paul had no armament against this.

Mrs. Winifred Balch, the stocky buyer of children's

clothes, stopped him one morning on the third floor. "Mr. Blaze, we ought to start a better back-to-school promotion," she said. "Did you see what Halliday's are doing?"

He nodded. Though Halliday's promotion was not an inspired stroke, they were advertising the gift of a lunch box to every school child for whom clothes were bought. How big an inducement this might be, he could only guess, but he doubted its effectiveness.

"Shouldn't we meet that with some promotion of our own?" Mrs. Balch said.

"If you've got any ideas."

The woman looked startled. It was usually the general manager himself who supplied ideas. She hadn't expected to be challenged. "Well, no—not exactly. I just think——" She glanced uncertainly around her department. "—we ought to find *some* way of bringing more kids into the store!"

"Sure," he said. "Let's try to dream up something."

He went on his way. Mrs. Balch looked after him uneasily, convinced that something was wrong.

Paul kept thinking about the possible sale, realizing this was the one act which could bring all his efforts to defeat. Whatever he might hereafter accomplish would be done for the Wolcott chain, not for himself, and he had no interest in Wolcott's. He certainly did not intend to spend his life as the manager of a Wolcott outlet.

True, Conrad Selby had assured him no final decision would be made for some time. Yet the president had appeared confident that the deal would go through.

The sense of frustration was still with him the week the Main Street windows featured Patrice's paintings.

For a time he had forgotten about them; but on this Monday morning, as he passed window after window, what he saw should have pleased him. In the left corner of each display a painting by Patrice stood on a small easel. The pose and costume of the mannequin beside it were accurate reproductions of the painted figure; and copies of the magazine lay open to Patrice's illustrations. It was all extremely effective.

Near the main entrance Paul met Patrice herself. She had obviously come to see how Ripley's staff had treated her work.

"It's wonderful!" she said. "They did a beautiful job!"

"Glad you like it."

"I'm supposed to meet a *Reporter* photographer here at ten. Wants a picture of me in front of one of the windows."

"Everett must have dreamed that up."

She looked very well this morning, he saw. Her eyes were extraordinarily bright. It was good to have *somebody* happy about all this. He was aware that Patrice was suddenly sober, inspecting him with the intensity that always made him feel he was being photographed in her mind.

She said abruptly, "Paul, you need a vacation. You look tired. In fact, you've looked fagged for days."

His laugh was dry. "I'm all right."

"What's bothering you? The Wolcott thing?"

"Of course."

After that she accompanied him into the store. She came all the way up to his office, her expression serious. When they were inside, she shut the door.

"You're taking it the wrong way," she declared.

"Am I?"

"The store hasn't been sold yet. I thought you were a smart operator."

"Overplayed my hand. I should have figured that when I started building volume some of the chains would become interested. Only, I saw Selby's as a sort of Gibraltar—something the family would never give up."

"They *won't* give it up! Not if you make them realize how valuable it can be—that the Selby boom has just *be-gun*——"

He looked at Patrice keenly. She could be right, he supposed. Perhaps his answer to the threat ought not to be surrender or even acquiescence, but redoubled promotion. If the future promised greater profits than Wolcott could possibly offer, why should anybody, even Conrad himself, dream of selling?

Paul sat down behind the desk.

"*I* don't want to see the place sold, either," Patrice said. "And I've talked against it. But the final argument lies in your hands. It's got to be an argument in terms of dollars and cents." She looked at her watch. "I've got to go down to meet that photographer—but think it over!"

When she had left, a glaze came over Paul's eyes. He leaned back, staring at the wall.

Promotion—more and bigger promotion. Beyond doubt there was logic in Patrice's advice. If he could make the Selby boom so big that no Wolcott price would seem attractive enough——

Surely there were many things he could do. Things *waiting* to be done. Like the problem Mrs. Winifred Balch had presented. He speculated over that a long time. . . .

Finally, with new interest in his eyes, he picked up the telephone. He asked the operator, "Who is Williston's superintendent of schools?"

"Dr. Seymour Parridge."

"Get him for me, please."

And presently, when a deep voice answered, he said, "Dr. Parridge? This is Paul Blaze at Selby's."

"Oh. Yes, Mr. Blaze?"

"Dr. Parridge, we have an idea for a civic project along educational lines—a social science contest for school children. But of course we wouldn't want to go ahead without your approval."

Caution came into Dr. Parridge's tones. "What kind of contest, Mr. Blaze? Generally, you know, we disapprove——"

"I understand. This one, though, is different. Here's the point: a store like this, Dr. Parridge, carries items from practically every country in the world. Laces from Switzerland, perfumes from France, leather goods from Italy, silks from the Orient, straw products from South America. Matter of fact, there's probably not a single member of the United Nations that isn't represented among the imported goods we carry."

Dr. Parridge said, "I suppose a department store *is* a sort of international bazaar. Yes."

"Exactly. Now what we have in mind is this: We'll arrange a display of fifty or so items from fifty different countries. Each item will be identified only by a number. Every school kid in Williston will be entitled to come in, look at the display, and decide for himself which country produces what. Selby's will award cash prizes to the youngsters with the most right answers."

Dr. Parridge was silent a while, then said, "That's an intriguing idea, Mr. Blaze."

"There's just one stipulation we'd like to make. It's all right for high school youngsters to come to the store alone— they can take care of themselves. But those below the high school level—we'd just as soon they were accompanied by parents."

"I understand."

"But as I say, I don't want to announce this contest unless it has your approval."

The superintendent's manner had changed. He sounded pleased. "Can't see any reason to disapprove of *such* a project. I should think every teacher of the social sciences would be delighted with it. A dramatic presentation of what the world produces—and of how the products of fifty nations are brought to the homes of Williston. . . . Excellent idea, Mr. Blaze. Excellent."

"Thanks. You think it's all right, then, if we go ahead?"

"Certainly."

Paul smiled. "Care to be one of the judges, Dr. Parridge?"

That brought a laugh. "I think, Mr. Blaze, you'd better pick your judges among heads of departments at the high school. *I* make a point of staying out of these things."

"All right. As you say. I'll get in touch with the high school principal. Thanks very much, Dr. Parridge."

When Paul hung up some of the old tension was back in his face.

They'd make the first prize $250. Then several prizes of $100 each; and a whole slew of 25- and 10-dollar prizes. If this contest didn't bring a few thousand kids and their parents into the store, he didn't know what would. . . .

Restlessness was back in him. He could feel it in his stomach. He got up and paced the office. He ran a hand through his hair.

Build up volume to a point at which no Selby stockholder will want to sell. . . . Patrice was right. That was the only answer.

There were other things, too, to settle today. When Randolph Green came back from New York, Paul summoned him to a conference.

"Green," he said bluntly, "I'm told we're overpaying on goods for the Paris Shop."

Though he had begun to sit down, the buyer arrested the movement. He stiffened. Then he lowered himself more slowly.

"Where did you get that?" he asked. "There are four stores handling the line. This is the first complaint I heard of anybody overpaying."

Paul handed him a sheet of paper. It listed the half dozen firms Bernardine had queried, together with the prices each had quoted. Randolph Green stared at it.

"Are—are these bona fide offers?"

"Absolutely."

Green raised suspicious eyes. "Bernardine?"

"She felt it was part of her job."

The buyer tossed the paper back to Paul's desk. He looked grim. "I see."

"Think you can get Cluss & Hein and Shantz to meet this kind of competition?"

"I—don't know, Mr. Blaze."

Paul studied the man's face, pale now. He could detect a nervous twitch of muscle. In a moment, he suspected, Green would have to eat one of his pills.

Paul went to the water cooler. As he filled a cup he said, "You puzzle me, Green."

"Do I? Why?"

"You're a damned good buyer. Best in the store. Yet every now and then you go off the handle on one of these cockeyed deals." Paul drank some of the water, fixed his eyes on the cup.

"Which is generally the situation when a buyer goes in for kickbacks. He's got to earn what manufacturers give him."

Green's face was suddenly colorless. He rose. The flesh at his jowls appeared to be trembling.

"Mr. Blaze, I——"

"Take it easy, take it easy." Paul sat down, made himself comfortable. "Ranny," he said, and it was the first time he had called Randolph Green by his first name, "I've been in this racket a long time. So have you. I don't have to kid you. You don't have to kid me, either. All I want is to keep you working for us. So I'm just suggesting that Cluss & Hein ought to meet these prices—or else let's transfer our business where we do get the best price."

This time Green was silent.

"Another thing," Paul went on. "You in debt? You need any quick cash?"

The direct question must have been a blow. Green drew a long breath. He said, "I—I owe *some* money. Who doesn't?"

"Much?"

"Couple of thousand. Why?"

"You'll make it up in bonuses this year. If it'll help, though, Selby's can advance it now. Just say the word."

Green started to answer, but the reply seemed to catch in his throat. He finally said, "That's—that's very decent of you, Mr. Blaze."

"Only, let's not allow anybody like Cluss & Hein or Shantz to play Selby's for a sucker. Everything else can be straightened out." Paul got up. "Do we understand each other?"

Green looked at him a long time. His face was still white. At last he said in a constricted voice, "I guess we do, Mr. Blaze."

"The name's Paul. . . . Think you can get these prices adjusted?"

"I—I'm sure I can, Paul. Thanks. . . ."

Chapter
Twenty-Five

WITH HIS RESURGENCE of spirit, Paul threw himself into work as he had never worked before. He was no longer striving only to increase Selby's volume; he was fighting to achieve the kind of success which would put the store beyond a selling price. He pressed with every idea that came to him, including the controversial plan to bring Santa Claus to Williston in a helicopter.

And his fervor was contagious. He could see his own rising excitement reflected in every co-worker. It was evident even in the way the Co-Workers Association prepared for the annual Anniversary Banquet, as though it were a special celebration this year. They had half a dozen committees devoted to the affair.

The 56th Anniversary Sale in early October—a full week's event embracing every department—was, as always, preceded by the Saturday night banquet. It took place in The Pavillion, a huge dance hall outside Williston. The Pavillion was a barn-like structure that had once been a skating rink; but for all its lack of architectural beauty it was the only place big enough to accommodate Selby's co-workers. The store now employed nine hundred and twenty people.

The executives and their families had two long tables of their own. At one of these Paul was seated between Patrice and Grace. Almost directly in front of him, at the next table, sat Bernardine; and it seemed to him her eyes and his were constantly meeting.

It was a noisy affair. The seven-piece band blared throughout dinner, playing from the stage. Part of the floor had been left clear for dancing, and many couples rose between courses. But the small floorspace was overcrowded; those at the executives' tables seemed content to wait until later, when the hall would be cleared and the dancing space made twice as large.

A group of co-workers entertained with skits. Since these concerned the tribulations of working in a department store, they proved intimate and hilarious; they lampooned everyone in Selby's with irreverent glee. In one sketch Paul saw himself impersonated by a man who rushed from department to department, his left hand waving a dollar sign, his right cracking a whip.

And when the show was over, George Weaver, the chubby master of ceremonies, stood in front of the microphone. He looked around, sweating and beaming, until there was silence. Then he spoke in the oracular voice so familiar to those who were accustomed to the Selby public address system.

He introduced a group of six co-workers who had been with the store more than 40 years. When the applause for them ended, he called on those who had served Selby's for 25 years. This time more than eighty responded. He called on the new general manager to take a bow, on several other executives. Then his tones changed.

"It is traditional at these dinners," he said, "that nobody

is asked to make a speech. And we won't break tradition to-night. However, I'm sure that this year you are all as proud of working in Selby's as I am. This is the year in which we are establishing a new record in serving the public of Williston. I think there's one man in this room who would be very happy to *hear* how proud you are to work for him. I think, too, that you're all as anxious as I am to show him just how you feel. So I am going to ask him to rise and take a bow—and I hope you'll bring down the roof. Co-workers of Selby's, it is my privilege to present the president of our store, Mr. Conrad Selby!"

Conrad slowly rose. Whoever had been playing lights on the stage now turned the spotlight on him. He stood in it, erect, gray-haired, smiling as he waved a hand.

And the applause was overwhelming. It came in a burst that welled up louder and louder, accompanied by the stamping of feet, the beating of spoons on glasses and dishes, the cries of co-workers who were not content merely to clap. And while Conrad continued to wave his hand, the band burst into a familiar tune. It caught the ears of the crowd even through the din, and within a few seconds more than nine hundred voices were shouting:

> *For he's a jolly good fellow,*
> *He's a jolly good fellow,*
> *He's a jolly good fellow,*
> *Which nobody can deny!*

Through it all Paul watched the president's face. He saw the muscles of Selby's jaws tremble as he struggled to maintain the smile. Finally he bit his lip and lowered his head, and when he sat down Paul wondered if he had seen tears in the man's eyes.

He glanced at Patrice. She, too, had looked down. She

seemed almost as moved as her father had been. . . . He bent toward her, starting to speak. Then he realized that at a moment like this it was wiser to be silent, and he said nothing.

Moreover, there was something else which kept him silent. It surprised him. It was hard to analyze, but he could find only one way of interpreting this feeling. He *liked* Conrad Selby. . . .

Yes, in spite of all their clashes, in spite of the strain and the antagonisms that had so often cropped up between them, he had to recognize a genuine affection for the man. Conrad might be obstinate and hard to handle, but in whatever he did he was sincere. An honest opponent. He believed in his principles and he clung to them. And in fighting for them he had always conducted himself with dignity.

In short, it occurred to Paul, Conrad Selby was the kind of man he himself would have liked to be. And that, when you considered it, had certain aspects of grim, paradoxical humor. . . .

When the demonstration for Selby subsided, George Weaver announced, "The waiters will now clear the tables and make room for more dancing. So we'll call a ten-minute intermission. Stretch your legs!"

Paul whispered to Patrice. "How about a breath of air?"

She nodded. He had felt instinctively that she wanted to get out of this heat and noise. More accurately, she wanted to recover from a moment of emotionalism. As he guided her through the crowd, toward an exit, he saw Bernardine again. Bernardine was watching him with a curious expression— watching as he led Patrice away—not giving any attention at all to the young man who was talking to her. . . .

Hundreds of cars were parked outside The Pavillion. Moreover, the co-workers were streaming out for air and a smoke.

So Paul took Patrice's arm and started toward the road. There were trees here, and they walked under them.

It was very dark. Patrice had drawn a wrap over her shoulders. As he glanced over her he thought she had never looked more attractive. She wore a black lace dinner dress with a flaring skirt, its belt line incredibly slim. Her blond hair had been set in waves.

She said, "Dad was—moved tonight. I—I've never seen him so shaken."

"It was quite an ovation."

"An evening like this *could* make him see that the new atmosphere of the store is a good thing. It could even make him see *you* differently."

"That would be nice, but I doubt it."

"He's never had so much applause before. It certainly must make him realize you've done him no harm——"

Paul said, "It doesn't matter. He'll always see me as an outsider trying to push him aside."

"Maybe not. In time."

"Even time can't change it. I'm not part of the family, so I'll always be an outsider to him." He uttered a tight laugh. "Which means, I suppose, that for the sake of harmony in the store I ought to get you to marry me. Make me one of the family."

Holding her arm, he could feel her stiffen. Instantly he knew he had said the wrong thing.

She looked up at him. "That was not very nice, Paul."

"I know. I'm sorry." His voice was almost inaudible, and he frowned at the grass. There was a sudden thumping in him, and he couldn't understand it. He had never felt this kind of nervousness before. He said, "It—it wasn't the way I meant it to sound."

"How *did* you mean it?"

"I don't know, Pat. Never before gave it any thought. Now that I've said it—well, it—it's got me hanging on the ropes. All of a sudden it seems like something I've been *wanting* to say——"

She turned abruptly, her face white. "Let's go back."

"Pat, I'm serious——"

"You're not. You're out on a limb, and you feel you've got to— Oh, let's forget it!"

He had an impulse to protest. But he choked the words. *What the hell's got into me?* he thought. Did he really want to marry Patrice? It was a wholly new idea. He scowled, not knowing what to say about it.

Because there were certain decencies to observe on an occasion like this, Paul danced not only with Patrice—though they said nothing more about marriage—but also with Grace, with Martha, with Everett's graceful wife, Betty. Finally, still aware of her frequent glances, he went to the next table for Bernardine.

They danced in silence for a time. Paul was thinking of other things. After a few minutes, however, Bernardine glanced up at his preoccupied face with a wry expression.

"Remember me?" she asked. "You asked me to dance."

He blinked, tried to smile. "Sorry, Berry. Off in a trance."

"All right for us to talk now?"

"Of course. Sorry."

"You look," she said, "as if you've just got a kick in the teeth."

"Can't imagine why."

"Everything okay?"

"Same as always."

She turned her face away. "You're not kidding me, Paul. Something's eating you."

"Forget it."

"Patrice?"

He glanced down at her again, frowning. "What do you mean by that?"

"Only the obvious. If you take the boss' daughter out for a long walk in the park, you've got to expect people to wonder."

"Berry, be yourself."

"I *am* wondering."

"Cut it out, will you?" If he sounded irritated, he could not help it.

"Well——" She smiled now, probably sensing she had gone too far. "I warned you I'm the jealous kind. Jealous as hell."

He was glad to have the music stop then; glad to take Bernardine back to her seat. And now he went outside again, but this time he went alone, to smoke a cigarette and think.

He was still astonished by the fact that he had talked to Patrice about marriage. He was even more astonished to realize the prospect seemed exciting and good, even compelling. He knew he could not allow it to remain unresolved, as if he had never uttered the words. He felt he had started something that had to be seen through to a conclusion . . . and it made his nerves pound.

Patrice, too, was preoccupied. Dancing with Everett and then with Ben, she scarcely spoke.

Paul's proposal, she realized, had been as casual and impulsive as his kiss at Hollow Lake. She ought not to give it much weight. Yet it disturbed her. Maybe disturbed was not the right word; the truth was it *excited* her. She hadn't felt so stirred since the first time Victor de Lange had kissed her that unforgettable autumn in Paris. Even Warren Graham, whom she liked, had never roused her like this.

Looking back over the past months, Patrice could almost measure, like tracing its course on a graph, the change in her attitude toward Paul Blaze. She had begun by resenting and disliking him. Then, somewhat grudgingly, she had been forced to acknowledge his ability as a promotion man. And in New York she had found certain unsuspected traits which she had definitely liked—a touch of humor, of ease, of honest self-appraisal. Whether she had begun to respect him then, she wasn't sure; it might have been later, when he had made his talk to the Borden graduating class.

At any rate, her feelings *had* changed.

And now that he had spoken of marriage—even unwittingly—she found herself, for the first time in years, giving earnest consideration to what marriage to a specific man might be. And in this case she saw that it could be stimulating, exciting.

Did all this mean she was in love with Paul? She didn't know. She was confused. She needed time to think. . . .

Conrad Selby could not go to sleep that night. Long after

Patrice had gone upstairs he sat alone in the living room, puffing at a cigar. More than an hour passed, and he remained unstirring.

At two o'clock in the morning he heard sounds on the stairs. Patrice came down, binding the belt of her dressing gown, her eyes troubled.

"So you can't sleep, either," he said.

"I've been waiting to hear you come up."

He put aside the dead cigar. "Pat, sit down."

She dropped into a chair, facing him.

"That banquet did something to me," he said. "Seeing that crowd of co-workers, realizing they represented what I had built, what I had put my whole life into——" He shook his head. "Pat, I can't sell them down the river."

"I never thought you would."

"Shows you what can happen to a man when he allows himself to be motivated by—by chagrin, by anger."

"By resentment of Paul Blaze," she said. "But Dad, he hasn't done anything cheap or undignified. The things you used to fear really didn't happen."

"Some are on the way now," Selby said. "Like his Christmas promotion."

Patrice frowned. She had heard about the helicopter stunt. She couldn't help sharing her father's compunctions.

"Maybe I'm wrong about such things," Selby said with a sigh. "Everything that's happened in the past six months seems to *prove* I'm out of step. So——" He paused. "Pat, I won't sell, but—I'm going to retire."

Patrice started.

"It'll simplify matters," he said. "And October 15th is the ideal time." That was the date of the Board's next meeting, coming just after the Anniversary Sale. "I want to step out,

Pat. Leave it to the younger men. I'm tired of fighting against things like this Christmas nonsense. The only thing I'm interested in is seeing that Ben is elected president after me."

Though she was dismayed, Patrice hardly knew what to say; he had so obviously reached his decision.

"One of the reasons I want to retire now," he continued, "is that this year the president couldn't be anybody but Ben. Or possibly Everett. But another year—who knows?"

"There's nobody else!"

"There's Paul."

"Paul? Oh, no! He wouldn't—the Board would never elect anyone outside the family!"

"I wouldn't be too sure. A year ago I'd have sworn the Board would never hire a *General Manager* who wasn't part of the family."

Patrice's glance shifted uneasily.

"Paul's ambitious," Selby went on. "And he's doing a good job. This year, Ben says, he'll probably hit close to eight million. If he promises them ten or twelve million the following year——" He shrugged. "Who knows? He'll be a stockholder by then. And, from what I've heard, I know he'd *like* to get himself elected president."

"Who told you that?"

"The man he used to work for—Edmond Christie. Met him in New York. He was joking, of course. But he assured me that if he knew Paul Blaze, Paul would some day wind up as Selby's president—even if he had to marry into the family to do it. He was joking, as I say, but I believe it's fundamentally serious."

The words hit Patrice like a blow. She bent forward, started to speak; but she could find nothing to say. . . . Suddenly she wanted to get away. To be alone. She urged Selby to go to bed, then ran up to her room. When she had shut the door, she looked at her pallid face in the mirror. And her eyes were stunned.

Had Paul's proposal been part of a premeditated plan? Another step toward securing a firm grip on Selby's? Self-promotion? Was he again trying to *use* her?

A shiver went through Patrice. She rose, threw off the robe. She got into bed, switched off the light. Then she looked up in the darkness, wide-eyed, too shocked to sleep.

Chapter
Twenty-Six

Two days after the banquet, when he came into the store, Paul went up on the escalator with Mrs. Winifred Balch. The buyer of children's wear was exuberant. "Mr. Blaze, that contest is working out fine!" she said. "We've had more than two thousand children come in!"

"Good. How's it affecting sales?"

Mrs. Balch rolled her eyes. "When two thousand youngsters drag their parents into the store—all I can tell you, Mr. Blaze, is that these past weeks have been 100 per cent better than the same weeks last year!"

Paul was not surprised. The International Contest, as he had named it, had done more than bring families into the store. The morning *Reporter* had run an editorial commending its educational value. He suspected, too, that the contest had been the subject of conversation in several thousand Williston homes. That kind of promotion was invaluable.

But when he reached his desk he sustained a shock that made him forget the contest. A memo lay there. He read it with narrowing eyes:

To all Members of the Board of Directors:

In order to allow you time to consider the matter of my successor, I am informing you now that as of October 15th I shall retire from the presidency of Selby's.

Conrad Selby

It gave Paul a wrench. He went into Selby's office, but the president wasn't there.

Maud Heller said, "Mr. Selby's gone to New York for the day."

So Paul walked down the corridor to see Ben Lork. "What brought *this* about?" he asked, holding out the memo.

Ben was impassive. "Can't say, Paul. Apparently he made up his mind Saturday night, at the same time he decided not to sell out to Wolcott's."

"Not to sell! Is that *definite?*"

"Yep. Notified the family yesterday."

When Mark Reickert drove into Williston to visit Martha, he was in excellent humor. Conrad's decision had restored all of Mark's optimism for his own future. True, it was disconcerting to find Martha in an irritable mood, but Mark did not allow this to trouble him very long.

"Personally," he said, "I think what Conrad's done is best all around. As far as the presidency goes, it's a break for Everett."

"For Ben," she said shortly.

"It needn't be Ben. Not if you and I don't want it that way."

She sent him a quick glance. "Does that mean you intend to vote for Everett?"

"Certainly. With Everett president and me chairman of the Board, the store can look forward to banner years. Both of us work well with Paul Blaze."

Martha was dropping sugar into a coffee cup. She checked her hand.

"Chairman of the Board?" she repeated. "We've never had a chairman of the Board."

He chuckled. "In the past six months we've established a lot of other precedents. No reason we can't establish this one, too."

"Forgive me if I sound crude, Mark, but—why you?"

"Elder statesman. Major stockholder. Why not?"

"I should think if we're *going* to establish the office, it ought to go to Conrad."

"Won't work. He's too much out of sympathy with this regime."

"Nonsense."

"Look, Martha. The man's *resigning* because he can't get along with the new setup. Why chain him to it?"

Martha shook her head. She gave Mark his cup, stirred her own. "After all," she said, "there are certain decencies. If there's to be a chairman of the Board, the position should at least be offered to Conrad."

Mark began to sound annoyed. "Why? If he's got any sense, he'll decline anyhow. He doesn't want to work with Paul."

"I for one could never face Conrad again if we didn't make the decent gesture. Besides, there's a more practical reason."

"I see nothing practical in electing him."

"Why throw away his years of experience? As chairman of the Board he'd be there to advise, to counsel, to guide. With all due deference, Mark, you don't know beans about running a department store."

"Now listen, Martha——" He put down his cup. "I came here tonight because I thought you and I might reach an agreement. Between us we can pretty well swing this thing. Especially if we can both work on Philip. I'll throw *my* weight behind Everett for the presidency provided——"

"Mark, stop it!" She became irascible. "I won't go into any secret deal that involves hurting Conrad like that! Even for Everett!"

Mark had thought this would be easy. Instead, he felt something slipping away from him—something he needed desperately for the sake of his self-respect. He groped for new arguments.

But Martha cut in, "I'm sure Everett wouldn't want it that way, either—by wounding his uncle. He's too fond of Conrad."

"Martha——"

"Let's drop this discussion. I find it distasteful. If there's to be a chairman of the Board, my first vote will go to Conrad. The rest will depend on whether or not he accepts."

There was finality in Martha's manner. She was, abruptly, the same dignified, positive Martha Selby who could so effectively dominate a club meeting. Inflexible. Wearing the Selby pride like armor.

Mark Reickert stared at her in dismay, with a rising sense of panic.

After Mark had left, Martha concentrated on her own problems. She had been deeply shaken by Conrad's decision to reject the Wolcott offer. It meant that there would be no windfall of cash. If she was to help Jerry at all now, she would have to revert to her original plan of borrowing on her Selby stock.

Pacing the living room, she warned herself it would be dangerous to make such a loan in Williston. She was too well known. There would be questions, speculations, even if they remained among the bank people. The transaction could be completed much more impersonally at a New York bank. . . .

With her stock certificates in her grip, she went to New York the following day. It was early evening when she reached the city, and she called Jerry from Pennsylvania Station.

He was surprised to hear that she was in New York. Behind his voice she could catch the music of his radio. And laughter . . . a girl's laughter. . . . It *could* have been in the radio, but it startled Martha.

She said, "I'll check in at the hotel, Jerry. Be with you in half an hour."

"Martha, look——" He seemed strained. "Why—why don't you wait at the hotel? I'll pick you up there."

"I don't mind coming down. It's always more pleasant."

"I've got a—a couple of friends here. Some of the boys." He lowered his voice. "I'll ditch them soon as I can, dear. Wait at the hotel, won't you?"

Martha accepted that as she accepted so many other things from Jerry Weed. But in the taxi, on the way to the Barkley, she began to wonder why Jerry had seemed so uneasy.

She discarded the obvious explanation of the feminine laughter. She considered jealousy a cheap thing to which she refused to stoop. Nevertheless, as she looked out of the cab's window, she frowned.

In the past year she had been stung a thousand times by doubts like these. Jerry seldom spoke of the women he knew. Whenever suspicion assailed her, Martha ripped it out of herself. It was easier not to wonder.

This time Jerry had mentioned "the boys." It occurred to her that she had never met any of his men friends, either. Not that she minded this. But *why* was Jerry so insistent on keeping her apart from the normal life he led in New York?

The trouble was that Martha knew the answer. She had known it, indeed, ever since the beginning. Only, she had never permitted herself to acknowledge it. Now, because she felt exceptionally calm and lucid this evening, she saw it clearly—and it left her stunned.

Jerry was embarrassed. He was reluctant to let his friends see that he was having this affair with a woman of fifty. . . . It wasn't the first time this had happened. She couldn't altogether blame him. Wasn't she herself ashamed to have him come to Williston?

"Here we are, ma'am," the cab driver said.

She paid him, walked into the hotel while a bellhop followed with her grip. As she registered, the clerk glanced curiously at her face. He had never seen Mrs. Selby so pale. Yet, when she walked away, she was erect and dignified—a very handsome middle-aged woman.

In her room Martha sat down and lit a cigarette.

During the past few minutes, because she had dared face an ugly fact, a change had come over her. Having allowed herself to view one truth with clarity, she now saw others.

This desperate act of raising money for Jerry on her stock —was it rational to indulge in such recklessness? *Why did no one else consider Jerry's play worth an investment?* Suppose it flopped. Suppose she lost the money she had been planning to put into it. That would mean the loss of her stock. What then? She had no other source of income.

Apart from her own well-being, there was Everett, too, to consider. As long as she owned stock she could vote to further Everett's position in the store. Certainly she owed that much to her son. If she were to lose the stock, however, Everett would be without his principal support. What she was doing, actually, was sacrificing Everett's future for Jerry. . . .

The thought crashed upon her like a blow.

With it came another appalling thought. Not that she hadn't been aware of it before; she had obstinately refused to consider it: *If she lost her stock, she would bring a New York bank into part ownership of the Selby store.*

That would end the family's secure hold on its heritage. She would be destroying what the others had kept inviolate. It would no longer be wholly a Selby enterprise, and even Conrad had not been able to bring himself to sacrifice that.

And for whom, for what, would she be doing all this? For Jerry Weed, whom she had not even known a year ago; for a play nobody else, not even its producer, considered worth an investment. . . .

Martha rose abruptly, unpacked her grip, hung a couple of dresses in the closet. When it was done she telephoned room service for a sandwich and coffee. Presently she sat by the window, eating, still thinking. An hour passed. Two hours, and three. . . .

Every minute increased the astonishment with which she had begun to regard herself. How could she have *dreamed* of doing so great an injustice to Everett? To the store? To the family? Even to her own future?

Suddenly she uttered a sound that might have been a laugh—a sound faintly touched with repugnance. She even shuddered a little. *I used to look in amazement,* she remembered, *at rich old women who hired themselves gigolos. I used to shrink from the sight, as if they were doing something horrible. But was it horrible? Wasn't it just—pitiful? As pathetic as this thing I've been doing?*

She thought about this a while.

No, it wasn't horrible, she decided. *Just sad and wistful and—and hopeless. Oh, so hopeless! A last try at youth—at recapturing something that can never be recaptured. And until you see that clearly and accept it, you haven't really grown up—you haven't really allowed your emotions to mature with your years. . . .*

It was after eleven when at last the telephone rang. Jerry's voice, still strained and apologetic, said, "Darling, I'm sorry. I just haven't been able to get rid of these guys."

She answered quietly, "It doesn't matter. I'm tired. I'm going to sleep."

"See you tomorrow?"

"No. I'll be going back on the morning train."

Jerry seemed dazed. "So soon?" His tone sharpened. "Anything wrong, Martha?"

"Yes, Jerry. I'm afraid I—I was over-optimistic. It's not going to be possible to raise the money."

"*Martha!*"

"One of those things, Jerry. Sorry."

There was stunned silence.

She said, "I'm exhausted now, Jerry. Let's just say good night." And as she put the telephone down she felt she was at last what Jerry Weed had never quite allowed her to be—a self-respecting middle-aged woman. It felt quite comfortable.

Chapter

Twenty-Seven

IN THE WEEK BEFORE the October 15th meeting Paul spent every available spare hour at dictation. He had a six-months report to prepare, and it was a good one. When Maud Heller finished the transcription, she had an eight-page document.

Paul took a carbon copy to the hotel. On Sunday he settled down to make necessary revisions. He worked in his shirt-sleeves, tieless, one leg thrown over the arm of his chair. When he came to the section that concerned Conrad Selby, he went over it several times:

It is most regrettable, in my opinion, that Mr. Selby has decided to retire from the presidency. He is so closely identified with the store, not only among the co-workers but in the public mind, that this is bound to be a shock to everyone. Since Mr. Selby is in his prime, healthy and vigorous, I am hoping that the Board may persuade him to reconsider his decision. He has many good years still to give to the leadership of the Selby Department Store.

Should he insist on giving up the presidency, however, it is my hope that he will accept the chairmanship of the Board of Directors. In this way his experience and his good counsel will not be lost to management. I would also urge, in the event of his retirement, that the presidency be continued within the immediate Selby family. The people of Williston have come to associate the store with the family. Any diversion from this pattern would, in my estimation, be an unfortunate and unnecessary blow to good public relations.

He came next to the paragraphs concerning plans for the future. One of them referred to the spectacular Christmas promotion.

It seemed to him that, theatrical as the helicopter idea might be, few spectacles would be more certain to attract crowds. So far nobody had produced a better plan; Paul was determined to go on with it.

He had come almost to the end of the report when he rose to answer the telephone.

"Paul?" Bernardine sounded worried. "Could I see you? I'm down in the lobby."

"Sure, kid. Come up."

He did not bother to put on a tie or a jacket; Bernardine was accustomed to his informality.

She wore a smart fall suit of Oxford gray. When she sat down, her fingers pattered on the bag in her lap. Paul, leaning back against a table, watched her in perplexity. It wasn't often Bernardine frowned like this.

"Paul, I'm in a spot."

"So I see."

"You—you've got to be frank with me."

"Baby, I'm never anything but."

Her troubled eyes rose to meet his. "Last night I was out with Roger Halliday."

Paul lifted one brow. His expression became partly sardonic, partly quizzical.

Bernardine said bluntly, "He offered me a job."

"No kidding."

"Head fashion buyer. The same job Randolph Green holds

here. And they'll pay me $2,000 a year more than Randolph gets."

Paul said without a change of tone, "They know what they're doing, Berry. Can't say I blame them."

"Oh, stop smirking!"

"I'm not smirking. Just admiring their good sense. They let Selby's build you up. They let Selby's send you to Paris and advertise your going and coming. They let Selby's turn you into a fashion authority. Then they hire you away. Damned good business. Provided, of course, you don't give a damn about things like loyalty."

"*I* didn't ask for it! They came to *me!*"

"Sure, Berry. I know."

"How far am I supposed to carry loyalty to this store? Is it a life sentence?"

"What did you tell Roger?"

"Nothing yet. First I—wanted to know what my chances are at Selby's." She looked down at the bag. "For a while I thought——"

"—that Randolph Green was on the way out?"

"Frankly, yes. But now he seems more solidly fixed than ever. If I stay in Selby's, where've I got to *go?*"

Paul's smile had a sad quality. "Reminds me of what a man named Christie once said to me: 'Once you're near the top you can't push much further.' . . . I don't know what to tell you, Berry. This is something you've got to decide for yourself. I'd hate to see you leave Selby's. You're good. You're tops. Don't know how we'd replace you."

Bernardine bit her lip. "Don't make it tough on me, Paul."

"Sorry."

She looked up with candor. "You know I'd rather work with you. But if this is all there is for me——"

"How far did you think I *could* promote you?"

"The—the kind of promotion I hoped for wasn't necessarily in the store. . . ." She rose, walked across the room to the window. He suspected she turned her back so that he would not see her face. And he felt uncomfortable. "Paul," she said, "nobody else is concerned about me—not anyone. I've got to look out for myself. This thing at Halliday's is a—big chance."

Paul contemplated his shoes. He was trying to hide the sting of Bernardine's words. To talk about loyalty, he knew, would sound hypocritical. Wasn't she doing to Selby's what he had done to Christie's? On what grounds could he protest?

He hated to see her do it. Apart from her value to the store, he was really fond of Bernardine. It had been good to have her around.

He supposed he could offer her an increase in pay. Still, he knew this was not what she wanted. She would never be satisfied, as far as her job went, unless she became the fashion head. And as for her private life, he suspected she would not be content until he asked her to marry him. . . .

Bernardine turned from the window. "They want their answer by the first of the month."

"It's up to you, Berry," he said quietly. "I hope you'll stay with Selby's. But you've come to the same fork in the road I faced six months ago. The only way to be happy is to make your own choice."

She drew a long breath. "In that case, Paul, I—I'll have to accept their offer."

He did not reply.

The problem of replacing Bernardine could be serious. At seven o'clock that Sunday evening Paul telephoned Conrad Selby about it. "Like to talk it over if you're free," he said.

"Yes, come along," Selby answered. "I'm dropping in to see Martha for a few minutes, but I should be back by the time you get here."

So Paul drove to the house on Warwick Hill.

On the way he became uneasy, primarily because of Patrice. Though he had seen her several times since the evening of the Anniversary Banquet, they had never been alone. He had, however, done a good deal of thinking about her.

When he entered the house, Conrad Selby had not yet come home. But Patrice was there. And he at once sensed a strange coolness in her manner. It surprised him. Were they back, in their attitudes, where they had been six months ago? Surely the fact that he had proposed, even involuntarily, could not have left her offended.

He tried for a while not to notice the change. Lighting a cigarette in the living room, he spoke as easily as he could. Nevertheless, he couldn't evade the fact that Patrice, when she spoke at all, replied almost in monosyllables.

After a time he could endure no more of it. "Pat, what's got into you?"

She sat on the couch, her arm stretched along its back. It seemed to him that she was looking through him.

"*Some* things I can't take, Paul."

"What now?"

"Like being used as a step to the presidency of a store."

Paul stared. "What kind of crack is that?"

"I'll say one thing—you were direct about it. Even when you talked about marriage, you made it clear it was for the sake of the store."

"Pat! You're not going to dredge *that* up again! Just because I——"

"It falls into the pattern. You *came* here because you wanted to get a grip on the store. You've worked at it every minute, day and night, for six months. You've grabbed every means you could find—including an attempt to use me." Though she spoke quietly, her eyes flared. "But you'll *never* get the store through me, Paul!"

He pushed himself out of the chair. His face was as white as hers, and his voice was choked. "Wh-where'd you pick up the idea I wanted anything like that?"

"It was part of your plan even before you came here. Isn't it what you told Edmond Christie?"

At first he couldn't understand. Obviously she or her father must have had some communication with Christie, but what on earth could the Philadelphia merchant have said to suggest this crazy notion? . . . And then, in a revealing flash, he remembered his last luncheon with Christie.

"Pat—you can't *believe* a thing like that!"

"It's what you told Christie."

"In a joke! In a smart-alecky exchange that didn't mean a damn thing!"

Now a taunt, almost derision, came into Patrice's voice. "Oh? You wanted to marry me for myself—is that it?"

"Damn it, yes!"

She too rose. She faced him with increasing anger. "You came here with ambitions that had nothing to do with me, Paul! Ambitions that were concentrated on the store!"

"That has no connection with my wanting to——"

"You hoped, one way or other, to become president."

"No!"

"It's what Dad believes. It's what I believe, too. Because

it fits in with everything you've done. Everything you've said!
. . . Oh, you'll come out all right at the end of the year.
You'll get your block of stock. But when Dad tells the Board
what you have in mind—eventually pushing Everett and Ben
aside as you've pushed Dad aside—I don't think you'll get a
renewal of contract for *next* year! There are some things they
won't sell out, no matter how high you build their volume!"

The front door closed. Patrice said, "Now you can talk
with Dad. As far as I'm concerned, there's nothing more to
say. Good night."

She turned and walked quickly out of the room. At the
door she almost collided with her father. He looked after her
in surprise as she went up the stairs.

"What's the matter with *her?*" he said. And then he
turned to Paul. "Sorry to have kept you waiting."

Paul was staring at the stairs. He hardly heard Selby.

Conrad said, "Sit down. What do you want to do about
Bernardine?"

"Nothing!" The word trembled with anger. Paul didn't
care about Bernardine now. He'd had more than he could take.
He certainly couldn't sit here and worry over a new Fashion
Co-ordinator. The hell with that. The hell with everything.
Rage against Patrice, against all she had said, blazed in him.
He said to Selby, "This Bernardine thing will keep. See you at
the store. . . . Good night!"

And while Selby looked after him in amazement, Paul left
the house.

Chapter
Twenty-Eight

An air of tension held the October meeting of the Board. The directors sat in their accustomed places at the long table, knowing that with Conrad Selby retiring, a new president would have to be elected today.

When he called the meeting to order, Selby seemed a trifle more solemn than usual. Aside from that, there was nothing to indicate this was the last meeting at which he intended to preside.

He planned to save the matter of his retirement for one of the last items on the agenda. Now he began by calling on Ben for the controller's report.

It was impressive, showing that in the past six months Selby's gross had exceeded $3,500,000.

"With the Christmas season still ahead of us," Ben said, "we may expect that the total for twelve months will be somewhere in the vicinity of $8,000,000. This, of course, is beyond anything we had anticipated. I think the Board has the right to congratulate itself on the prospects for the future."

While he listened, looking around the table, Conrad's eye paused on Martha. He wondered what had happened to her.

He had the uneasy feeling that she wasn't well. There were new lines in her face.

Mark Reickert, too, puzzled him. Normally he would have expected Mark to be enthusiastic about Ben's report. Yet Mark sat silent. Instead of celebrating the increased volume, Mark looked disappointed. In his case, too, Conrad Selby couldn't help wondering what had happened. Was it that they were all becoming callous to these big-figure reports? Could success lose its savor?

Or could it be, Conrad asked himself, that his own impending resignation threw a pall over these proceedings?

Ben finished and sat down.

Except for a slight stir, the report brought no response. No questions. No comments. Selby waited patiently. When it was clear nobody had anything to say, he drew a deep breath.

"Very well. We'll have the report of our general manager next. Paul?"

Paul rose at the far end of the table, buttoning his jacket. He was wearing a trim blue suit, a gray bow tie. His lips were drawn in tightly.

"I *prepared* a formal report," he said, "but this morning I tore it up."

The directors stared at him in surprise.

"I tore it up for several reasons," he said. "Whatever facts and figures you should hear, you have already got from the controller's report. As to what I myself have done during the past six months, there's no need to review the projects we launched. You're all aware of them. In the main they've been successful. They've borne out my contention that Selby's can look forward to vastly increased business in the years ahead."

He took the handkerchief from his breast pocket, touched it to his lips.

"When I came to this store I had only one purpose—to create a business boom. I knew that in the process I might step on a few toes. I might hurt people. I might even have to push a few aside."

This was not the kind of report they had expected. Some of the directors exchanged uneasy glances. Conrad Selby himself, having begun to take a cigar from his pocket, forgot it.

"If I have been any service to the Selby store in these past six months," Paul said, "I am, of course, pleased. These months—and especially the past few days—have taught me a great many things. Principally that I was wrong when I came here with the feeling that emotion, sentiment, call it what you like, had no place in business."

He was looking at the center of the table. His voice was low, and he did his utmost to keep it calm.

"I used to think that as long as I kept piling up volume I needn't worry about how people felt. In the long run, an increase of several million dollars would wipe out a lot of opposition. . . . That was a mistake. A very bad mistake in judgment. I've tried to assess what my six months here have meant to the store. In dollars and cents the results are good. In some other ways, however, they're bad—very bad."

His hands had been in his jacket pockets. Now he took them out, held the edge of the table.

"These six months have resulted in some bitter frustrations," he said. "Primarily I'm concerned with the frustrations they've brought to the president of this store. I can't help realizing it's because of my presence that he's resigning from something which means more to him than anything else in his life.

"This should not be allowed to happen. I see no reason for Conrad Selby's leaving the presidency. If there has to be a choice of his stepping out or my stepping out, there ought to be no question in anyone's mind as to what should happen. *I'm* the stranger here. The interloper. Somebody you hired to do a job. It's ridiculous that the president of Selby's should be uprooted for an outsider."

There was a stunned quality in the stillness.

Paul tried to find words that would make sense. His real trouble was that he could not tell them everything. Too much of it had to do with his emotional reaction to the contempt he had seen in Patrice.

He suspected that, like her, many of these people—whether they said so or not—must believe personal ambition was his only motivation in holding this job. Not that this was a stigma. Normally he would not have minded. But how could you go on working month after month when everything you accomplished must rouse the further contempt and distrust of people like Patrice, like Conrad Selby? Surely they would sooner or later communicate their feelings to the other members of the family. It was inevitable that all of them should come to regard him with distrust. A word from Patrice, a hint from Conrad, that he was striving for the presidency, could make even Everett recoil from him.

How much friendship, how much co-operation could he then expect?

Worst of all—and this was certainly something he could not say to the Board—was the prospect of endless friction and conflict with Patrice. He wanted none of that. He'd had his fill. There were easier ways to make a living. There were stores where he could work *without* emotional entanglements.

"My presence here," he said, "has had a disrupting effect. There's no need for this to continue. The store is moving along at a fine clip. Its volume will continue to increase. So I do no disservice to anybody—nor to my own obligations—by resigning. With me gone, Selby's can revert to the status quo. Its president can continue in office. There need be no upheaval. You all happen to be people I like and admire. I'm convinced my going will restore the peace and good sense that should characterize an operation like Selby's. And so, with the hope that my act will make Mr. Selby reconsider his own retirement, I'll confine my report this afternoon to the single fact that I'll be leaving you tomorrow."

He sat down.

The members of the Board gaped as if he had lost his mind. Again he took the handkerchief from his pocket, ran it over his mouth.

He knew he might have worked out the year of his contract. He might have waited to receive his stock bonus. But all that seemed unimportant now. It meant six months more of facing suspicion like Patrice's. Why inflict it on himself? He could devote these six months to finding a place with another store. It shouldn't be hard.

Everett, forgetting decorum, all but shouted, "What the hell's got into you, Paul?"

There was no way of answering him. It would have been absurd to speak of such a thing as sensitivity; to say that building business, even acquiring a block of stock, could be repugnant if in the process you lost the respect of those whose feelings meant most to you. . . .

At the Williston Hotel that evening Paul packed his clothes. The thing was done. His bridges were burned. The sooner he made the break clean, the better.

He folded suit after suit into the grips that lay open on the bedroom floor. In the morning he intended to drive out of Williston as early as possible. Why go through post-mortems with Everett, with Ben, with anyone else who might come up to protest? He supposed Bernardine would be here, too, before long—she had looked more shocked than anyone else at the conference table.

Yet Bernardine, he realized, was the last person who had any right to object to what he was doing. Wasn't she herself leaving Selby's? *Good old Berry*, he thought. *Always on the make*. He couldn't blame her. If your only aim was to get ahead, you couldn't afford to think of anybody except yourself.

He had been like that himself. The Malden boy on the way up. Ready to fight everybody and everything. And why? So that, in the end, he might become somebody like Conrad Selby.

Well, he had grown up. He'd learned something. People like the Selbys must not be defeated. They had to be preserved as ideals. They represented what all others like himself wanted to attain—dignity, respectability, integrity. Qualities like that had to be eternal; only a fool would try to destroy them or defeat them. . . .

At nine o'clock that evening, with his packing half completed, Paul remembered he had had no dinner. He picked up the telephone, ordered a sandwich, then went back to the grips.

A few minutes later, when he heard the knock, he went to open the door for the waiter. But there was no waiter.

He faced Patrice.

She stepped in quickly, a loose coat thrown about her shoulders. She wore no hat. Her blond hair looked wind blown.

It seemed to him, from what he saw in her pale face, that Patrice's nerves must be coiled as tightly as his own.

He slowly shut the door behind her. Whether she realized it or not, she was the sole cause of what he had done this afternoon.

Her voice was low, quick. "Paul, we have only a few minutes. They'll be here soon."

"Who?"

"Dad, Everett, Ben. I drove down first. I—had to see you before they got here."

He frowned. "Let's take one thing at a time. What do *they* want? Why the visitation?"

"There's been a conference at the house. Martha, Philip— all of them. They want you to stay."

He shook his head. "That's out."

"They need you and they know it. They've been at the house since five o'clock, working things out."

"Working what out?"

"You're adding $3,000,000 to Selby's business this year. Nobody else has ever been able to do a thing like that. Do you think they're going to let you go without a struggle to keep you?"

"Listen. I——"

"They've got everything arranged—provided you'll agree to stay."

There was another knock at the door. This time the waiter came in with the tray. When the man had left, Paul said almost harshly: "Will you please tell me what the hell's been going on?"

"Dad has agreed to become chairman of the Board. Ben will be president. Everett's to be promoted to vice president.

. . . It's all settled, Paul. They're all happy about it—and they'll spend all night to make you take back your resignation."

He was dazed and turned mechanically to the tray. He took the napkin off it, looked at the sandwich, but he was no longer hungry. Tossing the napkin back, he ran fingers through his hair. He turned slowly to Patrice.

"Let's have the rest of it," he said. "Why did *you* have to rush up here first?"

"To tell you how ashamed I am."

"You? What've *you* got to be ashamed of?"

"Myself. What I've said to you."

"You said what you thought."

"I'm ashamed because I was—so wrong."

Now his eyes narrowed.

She said, "Paul, *I* know why you resigned."

"Do you really?"

"And—it made me feel humiliated."

"Doesn't make sense. Why should my resigning hit you like that?"

"Because I thought nothing in the world was more important to you than getting yourself a—a piece of the store. Because I thought you'd go to any length to do it. . . . I know you're entitled to the stock you've been aiming for. All you'd have had to do would be to wait another six months, and you'd have had it."

"So?"

"But you're not doing it. You're throwing it away. . . . So there *are* things more important to you than stock, than——"

He seized her arms. His voice became hoarse. "Damn it, Pat, there are things a *hell* of a lot more important than a block of stock! But *you'd* rather listen to jokes by Christie!"

"Paul, I—I'm sorry. It was cruel. It was unjustified. I—I've come to apologize."

He swallowed hard then and released her. "Okay. Okay, forget it. . . . Can't blame you, anyway. Asking you to marry me *for the sake of the store*——" He finished with a bitter laugh. "Of all the cockeyed things to say, that was the worst I could've picked!"

"Why *did* you ask me to marry you?"

"Why does any man ask a girl to marry him? Because I love you!"

Something happened to her whole face. Her voice, too, became gentler. "Do you realize this is the first time you've said that?"

"Is it?"

"I—I might not have taken that proposal so casually if you'd said something about love. But you didn't. Never a word."

"If you want it straight," he said, "I wasn't sure then. I wasn't sure till I found out how much it hurt to have you turn against me—to see the contempt——"

"Not contempt, Paul. Disappointment. If I was disappointed, it was because I—I'd begun to love *you*."

He tried to answer, but he found himself inarticulate. There were no words for this. Suddenly he pulled her into his arms. He kissed her hard, almost angrily.

"Asking you to marry me never had anything to do with the store," he said. "You've got to believe that!"

"I do."

The telephone rang. He glanced at it in exasperation. It rang again, and a third time, and finally he went to pick it up. "Yes?"

Conrad Selby's voice was crisp. "Paul, we're down in the lobby—Everett, Ben and I. All right to come up?"

He glanced at Patrice. She put a quick hand on his arm, nodded. He turned back to the telephone. "Sure. Come on."

He had never felt so stirred about anything in his life. His eyes went over Patrice and he held out his arms.

"Before they come up," he said.

They made the most of the few seconds alone. And then, as she stepped back from him, she remembered something. "There's only one thing Dad's going to plead about—that Christmas helicopter."

Paul rubbed a hand over the back of his neck. After a moment he said, "It—it *does* seem kind of screwy, doesn't it? I mean—when you consider the kind of store it's been, the kind of family that's run it. I suppose a circus stunt like that *doesn't* match the tradition of dignity——"

There was a knock at the door. As he turned to answer it, he nodded at Patrice.

"They're right, honey. We Selbys don't want circus tricks. I'll dream up something more dignified."